POLARITY THERAPY
WORKBOOK

John Beaulieu, N.D., Ph.D., R.P.P.

BioSonic Enterprises, Ltd.
New York, New York
1994

Photography: Georgio Palmisano
Design, Illustrations and Layout: Pamela Kersage
Illustrations and Editing: Lisa Schimski
Copy Editing: Carolyn Clark
Modeling: Michal Briskman
Modeling and Editing: Thea Keats Beaulieu
Cover Design: Thea Keats Beaulieu

This book was made possible by a grant from
Synaesthetics, Ltd., a non-profit art foundation

ISBN: 0-9640604-0-X

Library of Congress number: 94-90579

First Printing September, 1994
Second Printing September, 1996
Third Printing April, 1999
Fourth Printing March, 2002

Printed in Canada

Dedicated to all students of Polarity Therapy

seeking to learn truth through healing.

ACKNOWLEDGEMENTS

I thank all the students of Polarity Wellness® from 1979-1994. The Polarity Therapy Workbook represents a completion of our relationship and the beginning of a new era.

I wish to acknowledge the Polarity teachers and practitioners from whom I have drawn inspiration and constructive feedback over the course of many years.

Schule fur Polarity Therapy, Zurich, Switzerland: Stefan Beutler-Huber, Marcel Bryner, Dominique Degranges, Ueli Gasser, Erica Grieder, Ruth Grutter, Alexa Haberthur, Marcel Hinze, Peter Isler, Marriane Konrad, Andreas Ledermann, Brigetta Ledermann-Raimann, Elsbeth Meurer, Corrie Pennings, Elisabeth Potesch-Schlumpf, Urs Rentsch, Peter Wydler

Ecole Romande De Polarite, Geneve, Switzerland: Simone Blanchard, Marilyn Velasquez-Chessex, Anne Zoe

Polarity Synergy, Zurich, Switzerland: Graham Dawson

Polarity Wellness® Center of New York, NY: Nanci Beaulieu, M.S., R.P.P.; Thea Keats Beaulieu, R.P.P.; Kathejo Bohlman, Director; Christine Bonnell, R.P.P.; Michal Briskman, R.P.P.; Vicki Genfan, R.P.P.; Adrienne Robbins, R.P.P.; Lisa Schimski, R.P.P.; Anne Seham, R.P.P.; Larry Tirino, D.C., R.P.P.

Polarity Wellness® of Lehigh Valley, Bethlehem, PA: Brian Kunsman, R.P.P.

Polarity Wellness® West, Santa Rosa, CA: Jan Milthaler, M.S.W., R.P.P.

Polarity Wellness® Center of New England, Boston, MA: Alaea Beynon, Lic.Ac., R.P.P.; Rex Beynon, M.A., R.P.P.

Polarity Healing Arts of Santa Monica, CA: Gary Strauss, M.S., R.P.P.

Wellness Institute, Santa Fe, NM: Jeff Jacob, R.P.P.

Linden Tree, Poughkeepsie, NY: Gary Siegel, C.S.W., R.P.P.; Regina Siegel, R.P.P.

Sound Health Studio, New York, NY: Frank Bosco, M.A., R.P.P.; Ellen Krueger, M.A., R.P.P.; Judi Rubin-Bosco, M.A., R.P.P.

Polarity Therapy, Dublin, Ireland: Heather Wolfe, R.N., R.P.P.

Lung Ta, Bloomfield, NJ: Marcus Daniels, Ac., R.P.P.

Carol Briskin, R.P.P.; Donna Defalco, Ms.T.; Susanne Durst, R.P.P.; Larry Galante, M.A., R.P.P.; Maria Gabriella Lay, C.P.W.E., Roma, Italy; Heather Rynd, R.P.P.; Iris Targoff, R.P.P.; Marcia Tumpowsky, Ms.T.; Reese Williams, R.P.P.

SPECIAL THANKS TO

My Mother and Father for everything.

My wife, Thea Keats Beaulieu, for being there in so many different ways.

My son, Lars Beaulieu, for always supporting my many projects.

My sister, Nanci Beaulieu, M.S., R.P.P., for her skills in management and her many contributions to the beginnings of this book.

Hans and Heidi Stager for providing an inspirational space for me to work in Zurich.

Sidney Rosenblum, D.C., for keeping me well adjusted.

David Barrett, Esq., for keeping me well counseled.

Satya Sai Baba for being in my life.

Dr. Randolph Stone, D.O., D.C., N.D., for giving us Polarity Therapy.

Chandana Becker, Ph.D., R.P.P., Raymond Castellino, D.C., R.P.P., James Z. Said, D.C., N.D., R.P.P., for sharing their keen insights based on their many years of experience.

Loel L. Resler, Th.D., Ph.D., and Mark Dargan Smith, N.D., of Westbrook University for their advice and support of this project.

I thank the people I served with on the American Polarity Therapy Association Standards Committee: James Z. Said, Philip Aberman, Damon Fazio, Howard Kiewe, Eleanora Lipton, Nancy Risley, and Kris Stecker, for trusting in the standards process and working so hard to make it a reality. Our interaction has inspired this book and added a new dimension to the practice of Polarity Therapy.

TABLE OF CONTENTS

REFLEXOLOGY PROTOCOLS

EXERCISE PROTOCOLS

STRUCTURAL ALIGNMENT PROTOCOLS

SPECIAL PROTOCOLS

BIBLIOGRAPHY

POLARITY SUPPORT PRODUCTS

Life is a song. It has its own rhythm of harmony.
It is a symphony of all things which exist in major and
minor keys of Polarity. It blends the discords, by opposites,
into a harmony which unites the whole into a grand symphony of life.
To learn through experience in this life, to appreciate the symphony
and lessons of life and to blend with the whole,
is the object of our being here.

—Dr. Randolph Stone

INTRODUCTION

Polarity Therapy is a healing art based on energy, what the ancients referred to as "Sacred Sound". Look upon this workbook as a guide for learning the basic scales and harmonic structures of Polarity. When you have trained your ears, eyes, and hands to listen, you will hear the music of Polarity.

Polarity is an ongoing process of relating to life energy. Learning Polarity gives us skills to help us meet our life challenges. When we face and honorably resolve our personal challenges, our understanding of Polarity deepens.

The professional practice of Polarity Therapy involves training in business skills and ethics as well as learning Polarity bodywork, counseling, exercise, and nutritional skills. The material in this workbook will help you reach your professional goals in the areas of bodywork, exercise, theory, and evaluation.

Every Polarity practitioner is different, and you can learn something new and feel something different everytime you have a session. You should receive as many Polarity sessions as you can. I have been practicing Polarity Therapy for twenty years and I receive at least one Polarity session a week. One of the greatest joys of being a student of Polarity is that students are always giving and receiving sessions with each other. When you graduate and start making money, find a way to continue receiving sessions. You will be a far better practitioner.

To develop and cultivate your personal creative and artistic expression of Polarity in professional practice, I suggest that you apprentice with successful practitioners. Every chance you get, be with and model these practitioners. Allow yourself to absorb their styles of practice. Eventually, your own creative approach will surface.

Always remember that the essence of Polarity comes from beyond all things. Be forewarned that, one day, the protocols and exercises in this workbook will disappear. On that day, the energy will call you. If you have done your homework correctly, your ears will open and your whole being will resonate.

Learn well, be strong of heart, and prepare yourself for the unknown. Trust, love, and when you are ready, give up the protocols and let the energy be your guide. Relax and enjoy the music.

John Beaulieu
Montauk, New York
December, 1993

POLARITY THERAPY OVERVIEW

Polarity Therapy is a truly holistic health system founded by Dr. Randolph Stone, D.O., D.C., N.D. Dr. Stone believed that life was much more than chemistry and that healing was greater than freedom from symptoms. He saw life as a spiritual journey and healing as the total alignment with that journey.

Dr. Stone's understanding of the healing arts began with the study of Western medicine which included structural manipulation, nutrition, and natural therapies. He then journeyed throughout Europe and the Far East studying different healing modalities. In the Far East, he studied Ayurveda, (the traditional healing system of India), acupuncture, yoga, and meditation. In Europe, he studied homeopathy and Hermetic philosophy and visited many nature cure spas.

Polarity Therapy is based on the premise that we are fields of pulsating life energy made up of specific frequencies known as the five elements: Ether, Air, Fire, Water, and Earth. Each element relates and flows in a balance of positive and negative attractions arising from a neutral center. When our thoughts, emotions, and physical body are out of alignment with the energy necessary to meet a life challenge, an energy imbalance results. These imbalances may appear as physical, mental, and emotional discomfort or pain. Polarity teaches us that this pain and discomfort is a signal for us to learn, change, and realign our lives.

An ongoing and dynamic balance of life energy is our foundation for health and well-being. Polarity Therapy helps us to develop this balance by promoting the flexibility, spontaneity, creativity, and clarity necessary to meet the challenges of everyday life. Dr. Stone says, "Obstacles are God's design to make man with a spine." We must have challenges to grow spiritually. Meeting these challenges is a life-long process in which we learn to increase the depth of our understanding and awareness and apply this to every moment of our lives.

A Polarity practitioner utilizes the tools of bodywork, exercise, nutrition, and verbal guidance to evaluate and balance life energy. Polarity bodywork involves gentle rocking, stretching, and pressure-sensitive touch based on energy flow. Polarity exercises are easy stretching postures combining sound, breath, and self-massage. Polarity nutrition views food as energy and develops an ongoing, ever-changing, and creative nutritional awareness rather than a rigid set of rules. Polarity verbal guidance is based on the assumption that "right thinking" is the cornerstone of good health. Verbal processes involve understanding and feeling our emotions, taking responsibility for our lives, and creating life-enhancing thoughts.

Today, Polarity Therapy is under the guidance of the American Polarity Therapy Association (APTA). APTA maintains a registry of professional Polarity practitioners. It also accredits professional Polarity Therapy courses, upholds high ethical standards, and interfaces with other healing arts professions. Through the APTA, Polarity Therapy practitioners can continue to develop the practice and art of Polarity Therapy.

HOW TO USE THE POLARITY THERAPY WORKBOOK

The purpose of the *Polarity Therapy Workbook* is to provide a structure for learning the art of Polarity Therapy.

Structure, represented by the six-pointed star, is the masculine principle of Polarity Therapy. Structure creates the space for learning. That space must be filled with expressive and creative energy. Structure without expression leads to decreased life energy. Structure with expression leads to growth, joy, success, and the thrill of learning.

I trust that you and your teachers will fill this workbook with the expressive and creative qualities of Polarity Therapy. The workbook, like Dr. Stone's "oval fields," has many open spaces for your notes, drawings, doodles, and insights.

The *Polarity Therapy Workbook* is an easy-to-read guidebook of pictures and protocols for the beginning as well as the advanced practitioner of Polarity Therapy. The workbook is designed to help you learn new skills, review the ones you already know, and practice the art of Polarity Therapy. Dr. Stone believed that learning requires "burning the midnight oil." The *Polarity Therapy Workbook* is one of many candles to help you through the night. May the Light be with you.

HOW TO USE THE PROTOCOLS

I compare my experience of learning Polarity Therapy to my experience of learning the ancient Chinese martial art of Tai Chi Chuan. The Tai Chi symbol is the same as the Polarity principle of life energy...

...It is an empty circle which contains both negative and positive forces within it. The ancient Chinese called these forces *Yin* and *Yang*. Dr. Stone called this empty circle "neutral", the Yang force "positive", and the Yin force "negative". These forces continually interact to create all life.

For thousands of years, Tai Chi has been taught with protocol movements called "forms" combined with readings in the Tai Chi classics. Each Tai Chi form contains the principles of the Tai Chi classics expressed in movement. When you practice the form correctly, your physical body aligns with these principles. Every time you reach a new degree of alignment, the Tai Chi classics must be studied again. This process creats an ongoing energetic connection between the mind and body.

In the *Polarity Therapy Workbook,* the protocols provide a systematic method of learning and practicing important Polarity principles and skills. Learning the protocols is similar to practicing the Tai Chi forms, just as studying Dr. Stone's writings is similar to reading the Tai Chi classics. Learning Polarity Therapy is a life-long process. Be patient and take your time. There is always something new to discover.

It is best, if possible, to learn the protocols in a class taught by a qualified instructor. Your instructor will teach you the principles necessary to perform these protocols. You can then look at the pictures and make notes in your workbook. When you practice, open your workbook to the picture and place yourself in the proper position to perform each move. When you receive correction from your instructor, associate the feeling of the correction with the picture, the description of the move, and your notes. When you practice at home, the workbook will help you remember the moves.

After you have practiced a protocol several times and begin to feel the flow of the moves, then it is time to read Dr. Stone.

HOW TO USE THE REFERENCES TO DR. RANDOLPH STONE'S *POLARITY THERAPY VOLS. I & II* AND *HEALTH BUILDING*

I have been learning, practicing, and teaching Polarity Therapy for twenty years. Every time I read and re-read Dr. Stone, I am both humbled and inspired. I remember the first time I looked at one of Dr. Stone's charts. I was sitting at my desk at Bellevue Psychiatric Hospital when a dance therapist on staff placed a copy of Dr. Stone's Composite Energy Chart on my desk. She said, "I thought you might like this. What does it mean?" I glanced at the chart and felt as if I was going into a trance. My eyes followed the patterns of the picture until I discovered the words "Ultra-Sonic Core." I stayed there for what seemed to be a very long time, and then I looked up at the therapist and said, with all my therapeutic wisdom, "I don't know."

That was my first introduction to Polarity Therapy, over twenty years ago. Now, after countless hours of reading Dr. Stone, I still have that same feeling when I look at his charts. I go back to my Polarity practice with my mind spinning, feeling a great reverence for the depth and scope of his work. I know I will be looking at these charts for the rest of my life.

When a student tells me that Dr. Stone is confusing to read I always reply, "Only if you are *trying* to understand."

With this in mind, I urge every one of you to read and re-read the works of Dr. Stone. To help you begin, many parts of this workbook are referenced to Dr. Stone's books, now available in three volumes:

Health Building: HB

Polarity Therapy Vol. I

    Book I: Bk I

    Book II: Bk II

    Book III: Bk III

Polarity Therapy Vol. II

    Book IV: Bk IV

    Book V: Bk V

    Evolutionary Energy Series: EES

    Energy Tracing: ET

    Advanced Notes: AN

For example:

    (Bk II, Ch 3) refers to *Polarity Therapy Vol. I*, Book II, Chart 3.

    (EES, Ch 4, 6) refers to *Polarity Therapy Vol. II*, Evolutionary Energy Series, Charts 4 and 6.

Polarity Therapy Vol. I, *Polarity Therapy Vol. II*, and *Health Building* are published by CRCS Publications, Post Office Box 1460, Sebastopol, CA 95472, and can be ordered through any bookstore.

HOW TO USE THE APTA STANDARDS REFERENCES

The American Polarity Therapy Association *Standards For Practice* document sets national standards for Polarity practitioners. Every student, practitioner, and instructor of Polarity Therapy is accountable to this document. The *Standards For Practice* document can be obtained from the American Polarity Therapy Association headquarters.

The references to the *Standards For Practice* will be found in brackets [ ] after bodywork moves and notes; the abbreviations used refer to the following sections of that document:

    Bodywork: BW

    Energetic Nutrition: EN

    Evaluation: EV

    Stretching Postures: SP

    Theory: TH

For example:

[BW: V.A.1a] refers to the bodywork section, numeral V, subdivision A, number 1, subdivision a.

[EV: 4a] refers to the evaluation section, number 4, subdivision a.

These references are especially valuable to instructors and course designers who must understand and communicate the standards to students.

HOW TO DESIGN YOUR OWN PROTOCOLS USING THIS WORKBOOK

Each protocol contains a sequence of bodywork moves. The sequence can be rearranged according to your own individual learning or teaching style. This is of special value to course designers wanting to meet American Polarity Therapy Association course registration requirements.

To create a new protocol, look through the pictures and make your own sequence list. Reference your list to the names and pages of the bodywork/ exercise moves in the workbook. Then give the new protocol sequence to your students and have them insert it in their *Polarity Therapy Workbook*. Your protocol is now automatically referenced to the APTA standards and Dr. Stone's books.

HOW TO USE THE EVALUATION AND THEORY NOTES SECTIONS

Many protocols are followed by Theory and Evaluation Notes. These may be referenced to Dr. Stone's books, the APTA Standards For Practice, and/or other related texts. These notes outline the theory and evaluation skills necessary for understanding the protocols. I suggest you enhance your understanding and skills by asking questions of your Polarity instructor and reading the suggested references. References are given by abbreviated book name and page number. The full names of these books can be found in the bibliography.

Example: (*Polarity Process*, pp. 26-31). To understand this reference look up *The Polarity Process* in the bibliography, purchase the book, and read pages 26-31.

HOW TO USE YOUR WORKBOOK AS PART OF A HOME STUDY PROGRAM

When you are not near an instructor or school, you can use this workbook as a guide to learn the basics of Polarity Therapy. The best way to pursue home study is to utilize the workbook in conjunction with special audio and video tapes. These tapes are available through the Polarity Wellness® Network. They are referenced to the protocols and make excellent study aids. To inquire, call 1-800-925-0159.

Notes

STUDENT AND PROFESSIONAL GUIDELINES

The following guidelines are to help you maintain basic ethical standards and proper boundaries during your protocol sessions. Boundaries create a safe space for growth—for you and your client. Read each of the guidelines carefully. Ask your instructor to explain them if you have the slightest doubt about their meaning and application.

1. *Non-prescription drugs:* Do not take non-prescription drugs before or during protocol sessions. Dr. Stone was adamant that drugs and alcohol should not be used. Not only do they interrupt the free flow of energy, but they alter consciousness in ways which inappropriately affect our judgement. It is unethical to be using drugs or alcohol in conjunction with sessions.

2. *Proper Boundaries:* Do not sexualize protocol sessions. Sexualizing of sessions includes inappropriate suggestions, masturbation, inappropriate fondling, oral sex, and any sort of sexual penetration. If you become interested in your client and want to form a relationship outside of the therapeutic environment, discontinue your professional relationship with the client. Sexual misconduct has serious professional, legal, and ethical consequences both for the client and for the practitioner.

3. *Confidentiality:* Do not reveal the content of your sessions. If you keep documentation, make sure it is in a safe and secure place.

4. *Professionalism:* Do not advertise or claim to be a professional Polarity practitioner until you have completed the minimum requirements for Associate Polarity Practitioner as set forth by the American Polarity Therapy Association and have fulfilled the necessary legal requirements in your area.

5. *Finances:* Do not charge for a Polarity session until you are qualified as an Associate Polarity Practitioner and have fulfilled the necessary legal requirements in your area.

6. *Limitations of Practice:* At all times, accurately represent your level of Polarity competence, education, and experience.

7. *Responsibility:* As a Polarity student, you should recognize that your actions and suggestions have a significant impact on the lives of others. Always strive to represent Polarity in the highest light through the example of living the principles in every aspect of your daily life.

8. *Respect for Others:* Our goal is to assist another person on his/her life path through teaching the correct use of Polarity energy principles. We recognize that we are in a respected and powerful position and that our words and actions have a profound effect on our clients. We endeavor to always support and nourish the life force and honor our clients.

Notes

PREPARATION FOR GIVING A POLARITY PROTOCOL SESSION

1. Make sure your practice room is comfortable and safe. Your client will not be able to relax in an environment with people walking through, phones ringing, and other distractions. Your treatment table should be strong and secure. If you are working on the floor, work on a futon or comfortable pillows.

2. Establish clear time boundaries. Let your client know how long you are going to practice and hold yourself to within five minutes of this. It is important that your client get the message that you keep your word. This establishes trust. If you want to change the boundary, then negotiate it with your client. You must learn the art of timing a session to have a successful practice with clients scheduled every hour or half hour.

3. Wear comfortable cotton clothing and advise your client to wear the same. Cotton is a natural fiber which does not inhibit energy flow and is easiest to work with.

4. Have your client lie down. Sit at the head of the table and center yourself, i.e., pause, take a deep breath, close your eyes for a minute, and be with yourself. You may also choose to begin by sitting or standing at your client's feet or torso.

5. Say an affirmation to yourself that establishes your intention, e.g., "I place my work into the light for the highest good."

6. Rub your hands together and slowly bring your hands toward your client's body. Notice your sensations and feelings as you allow yourself to merge with their energy. If you feel any resistance, stop and wait.

Notes

GENERAL SESSION PROTOCOL INTRODUCTION

The general session protocol was developed by Pierre Pannetier, N.D. It is an excellent introduction to Polarity Therapy. Learning and practicing the general session teaches you how to prepare for and give a Polarity session. You will learn how to safely touch another person, how to maintain proper boundaries between client and practitioner, and how to tune into life energy. It also sets the tone for an initial understanding of positive, neutral, and negative polarities and their relationship to rajasic, satvic, and tamasic qualities of touch.

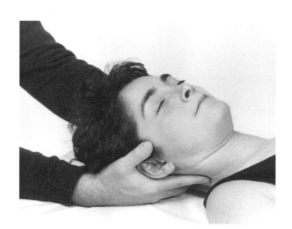

I first learned the general session in 1973 from a friend. He had just returned from California and said, "Let me give you a Polarity session. You'll love it." I lay down on the floor and he proceeded to give me my first Polarity session. It was the general session and I was in heaven. I said, "Could you teach me how to do that?" He said he would show me the moves. So I learned the general session. I couldn't wait to practice it on everyone. During the next year, I did over three hundred general sessions. I was hooked.

To this day, I am amazed at the wonderful results I obtained through just giving a basic general session. Whenever I get caught up in Polarity theory or some aspect of Polarity practice, I recall my simple beginnings. With a loving intention and proper boundaries, Polarity will unfold on its own. For me, the general session is like a seed. When you learn, practice, and give the general session, you nourish the seed, allowing Polarity to grow in your consciousness.

The purpose of learning the general session is to learn how to touch, give a session, and develop a feeling for the work. I suggest that you read Richard Gordon's *Your Healing Hands* as the primary reference book for this protocol. Because the general session moves will appear in different forms throughout this workbook, I have given only a few references to Dr. Stone. They will be specifically referenced in later protocols. For the moment, focus on the art of giving a session.

GENERAL SESSION PROTOCOL

1. Cradle

2. North Pole Stretch

3. Right & Left Side Occipital Press

4. Tummy Rock

5. Brushing Off Legs

Right & Left Side:

6. Lean & Pull

7. Toe Pulls

8. Knuckle Rub

9. Inside Heel Press

10. Outside Heel Press

11. Flexed Tendon Press

12. Cuboid Ankle Rotation

13. Collar Bone/Solar Plexus Rock

14. Thumb Web & Forearm Stimulation

15. Finger Pulls

16. Hand & Foot Diagonals

17. Crown Spread

18. Forehead & Navel Balancing

19. Brushing Off

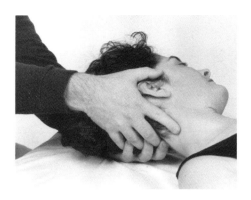
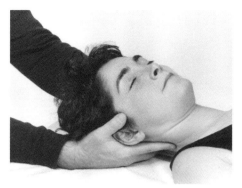

Cradle: Keep your hands soft and relaxed. The touch is satvic. Your index fingers go down the sides of the neck, your middle fingers cross at the occipital base, and your thumbs rest by the ears. The head should be entirely cradled in your hands and not touching the table.

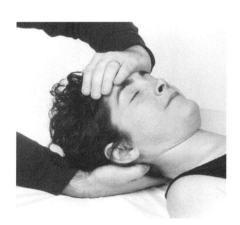

North Pole Stretch: Rest the head on the palm of your right hand, lightly grasping the occipital base on either side of the cervical spine with your middle finger and thumb. Place your left hand on the forehead. Apply a steady superior traction with your right hand.

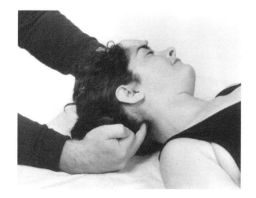
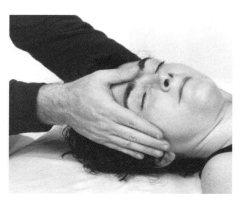

Right and Left Side Occipital Press: Turn the head to the left so that it is tilted at a 45° angle. Using the index or middle finger of your right hand, press into the soft tissue on the right side of the occipital base. Place your left hand diagonally opposite on the forehead. Visualize energy crossing in a diagonal from your right finger to the palm of your left hand. The pressure at the occipital base may be satvic to tamasic. Do both sides.

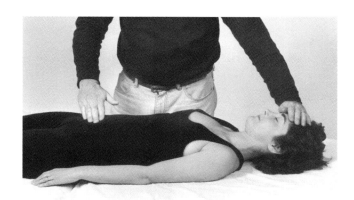

Tummy Rock: Rest your left hand gently on the forehead and your right hand about 1½" below the navel. With your right hand rock rhythmically (rajas). Stop and feel the energy (satvas).

Brushing Off Legs: Place your hands lightly below the knees and brush downward toward the toes. At the end of the sweep, let your hands lift upward and lightly shake them. You may do this several times.

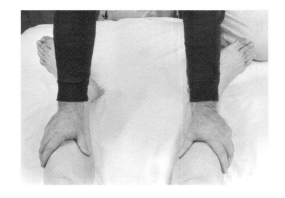

Lean and Pull: Rest the heel on the palm of one hand and grasp the ball of the foot with your other hand. Lean forward (superiorly) on the foot using your body weight to give the Achilles tendon a good stretch. Then place your hand over the center of the top of the foot and pull downward. The two movements should create a gentle pumping motion. Repeat several times.

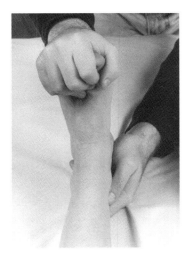
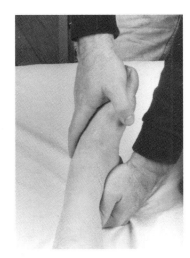

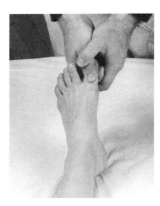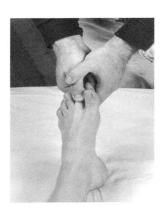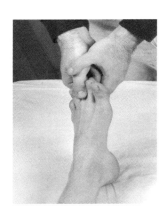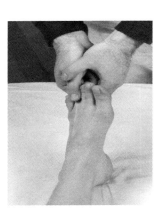

Toe Pulls: Firmly grasp the base of the big toe between your thumb and index finger. The index finger should be bent at a right angle. Place your other hand around the first for support as shown. Relax your arms and shoulders and, moving from your center, gently pull the toe downward (inferiorly), allowing your body weight to do the work rather than your forearms. At the end of each pull you may also lift the toe and shake it rhythmically. Be gentle. Repeat for the other toes.

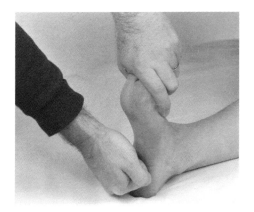

Knuckle Rub: Make a fist with one hand and grasp the toes and top of the foot with your other hand. Pull backward to open up the foot while sliding your knuckles upward.

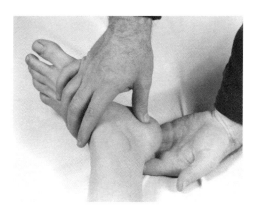

Inside Heel Press: Support the heel of the foot with your fingers. With the thumb of your other hand, find a sore spot on the inside of the heel. Press steadily and firmly (tamas) into the sore spot. Be sensitive to your client's boundaries and always ask for feedback. *Warning: This area contains the reflex for the uterus. Do not press during pregnancy.*

Outside Heel Press: Support the foot with the fingers and palm of one hand. With the thumb of your other hand, locate a sore spot on the outside of the heel. Press steadily and firmly (tamas) into the sore spot. Be aware of your client's boundaries and ask for feedback. *Warning: This area contains the reflex for the ovaries. Do not press during pregnancy.*

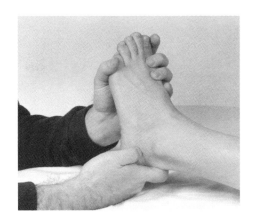

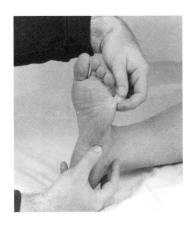 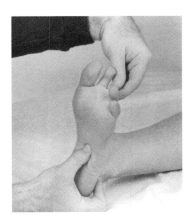 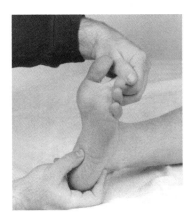

Flexed Tendon Press: With the thumb and index finger of one hand, grasp the small toe, stretching it upward and back (superiorly). With the thumb of the other hand, "walk up" the tendon from the heel to the base of the toe. Repeat with the other toes.

Cuboid Ankle Rotation: Side bend the foot toward the midline, place your thumb on the cuboid bone (halfway between the heel and toes), and press upward toward the base of the fifth metatarsal. Deepen the pressure by rotating the foot back into your thumb.

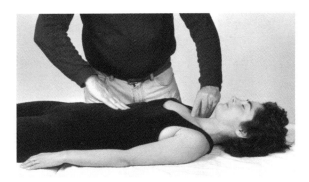
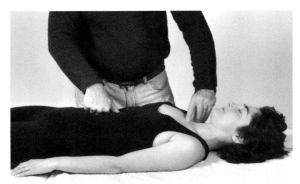

Collar Bone/Solar Plexus Rock: Place your right thumb on the side of the abdomen just below the rib cage. The index finger of your left hand makes contact with the head of the collar bone near the center of the neck and your fingers grip the body of the collar bone. As your client breathes in, rock the collar bone back and forth. And, as your client breathes out, press inward in the direction of the opposite shoulder with your right thumb and gently rock. Continue breathing and rocking, allowing your right thumb to move inward along and just underneath the rib cage toward the solar plexus. Do both sides.

Thumb Web and Forearm Stimulation:
Find a sore spot in the web between the thumb and index finger and squeeze. With the thumb of your other hand, find a sore spot on the inside of the elbow toward the outside of the arm. "Ping-pong" between the sore spots.

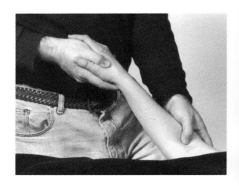

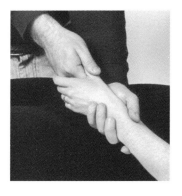
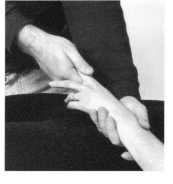

Finger Pulls: Grasp the base of the thumb between your thumb and index finger. Hold the wrist with your other hand. Gently and firmly pull the thumb away from the wrist, allowing your fingers to slide from the base toward the tip (distally). Repeat for the other fingers, ending with the little finger.

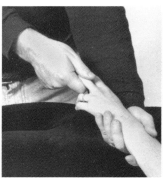
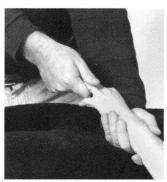

Hand and Foot Diagonals:
Gently hold the thumb of one hand and the big toe of the opposite foot. Do both sides.

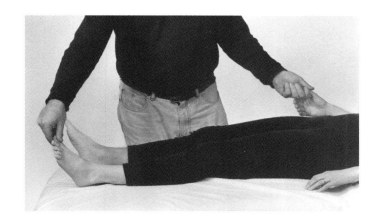

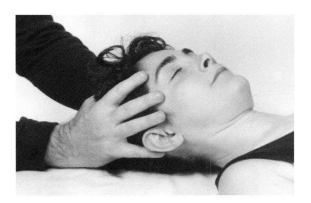

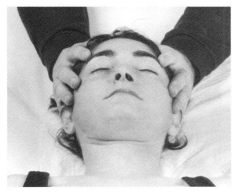

Crown Spread: Evenly spread your fingers around the head with your little fingers at the back of the ears (mastoid process), your ring fingers in front of the ears (TMJ), your middle fingers near the temples (sphenoid), your index fingers on the forehead (frontal), and your thumbs on the top of the head (parietal).

Forehead and Navel Balancing:
From the right side of the body, make soft fists and let the thumbs point outward and down. Gently touch the right thumb on a spot about 1½" below the navel. The left thumb should make no physical contact and is placed above the center of the forehead at the "third eye."

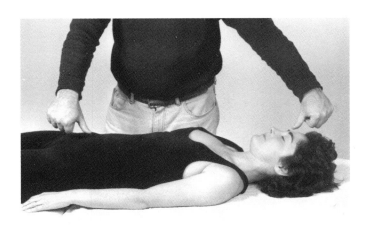

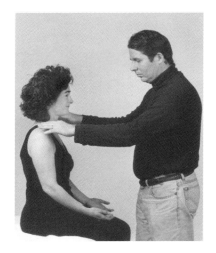

Brushing Off: Begin with both hands at the shoulders. Your client's palms should be facing upward. Quickly and lightly sweep down the arms and over the palms, lifting your hands upward at the end of the sweep. Do this several times.

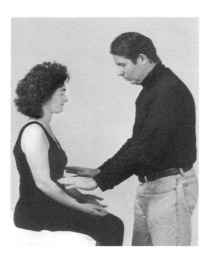

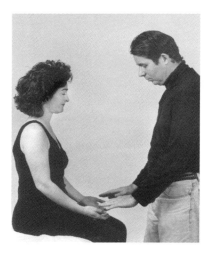

GENERAL SESSION NOTES

WHAT IS LIFE ENERGY?

(Bk I pp. 8-21; HB pp. 11-14)

Key words: Prana, Chi, Ki, Life Force...

POLARITY ENERGY PRINCIPLE

(Bk I p. 14, Ch 3) (*Polarity Process*, pp. 1-32)
[TH: I.A,B,C]

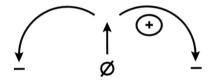

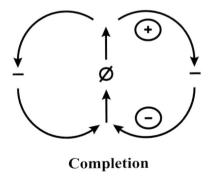

Completion

THE THREE PRINCIPLES RELATED TO TOUCH, NUTRITION, AND ENVIRONMENT

(HB pp. 15-16) (*Polarity Process*, pp. 104) [TH: II.B]

Touch

Satvas: light touch

Rajas: rocking, stimulating

Tamas: deep, penetrating, dispersing

In relationship to touch, the three principles should be defined in terms of your client's response rather than a preconceived idea. Dr. Stone states: (Bk II pp. 65-66)

    Satvas: "This must be so fine that it is imperceptible to the tissues and does not arouse them to reaction."

    Rajas: "...must have momentum, but no compulsory force which causes a reaction..."

    Tamas: "This is the type of therapy where there must be a reaction of soreness, due to greater activity of the re-established life force and circulation in these areas."

Nutrition

Satvas: fresh fruits and vegetables

Rajas: cooked grains

Tamas: meats, fermented foods

Environment

Satvas: light, airy, relaxed

Rajas: constant movement

Tamas: dark, enclosed, intense

DESCENT OF SPIRIT INTO MATTER

(Bk I pp. 54-56) (*Polarity Process*, pp. 1-32) [TH: V.A, C]

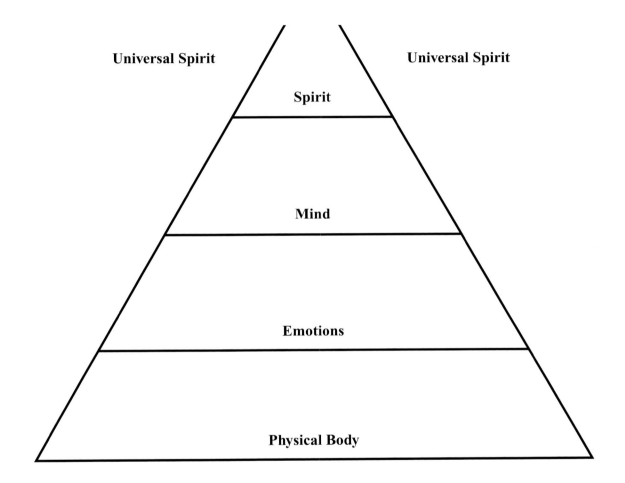

BASIC POLARITY RELATIONSHIPS

(Bk II Ch 5,6,7) (*Polarity Process*, pp. 34-36) [TH: III.E]

The top of the body has a positive charge.

The feet have a negative charge.

The right side has a positive charge.

The left side has a negative charge.

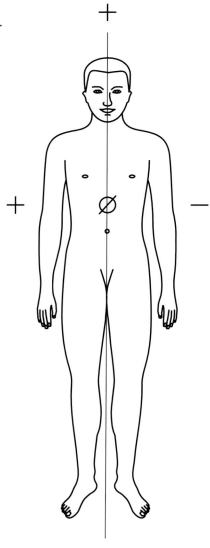

Notes

ELEMENT PROTOCOL INTRODUCTION

The purpose of the element protocols is to learn and practice the art of tuning into elemental energies. Just as musical scales are the foundation for creative composing, so the element protocols are the foundation for the practice of Polarity Therapy as a healing art. Instructors are always creating, adding, and subtracting moves from these protocols. This is because feeling and working with the elemental energies is more important than focusing on precise bodywork skills.

When learning and practicing the element protocols, you should allow yourself to become aware of different qualities, mixtures, and shades of elemental energies. The elements become like a keyboard of expression. Ideally, when we are confident enough, we can "tune into" and evaluate a client's energy and create a unique session.

The exercises provided at the beginning of each element protocol are to guide you into the "feeling tone" of the element [TH: V.C]. Working with these exercises will help you understand elemental energy by having a direct experience. When you allow yourself to resonate with the experience of Ether, Air, Fire, Water or Earth, the protocols come alive. Your hands then become like elemental tuning forks.

The next step is to learn to tune into the energy and identify the qualities which manifest when someone, including yourself, is resonating with different elemental energies. For example, wind is invisible. However, by closely observing a tree, we can observe the different effects of the wind moving the branches and leaves. By observing ourselves and our clients, we can learn to recognize the different elemental qualities moving through us. Cultivating this ability is the beginning of good Polarity evaluation skills.

When learning these protocols, it is best not to focus on or make relationships between energy and anatomical/medical model thinking. To do so tends to disconnect us from the experience of the energy. When we start thinking in "cookbook" terms, i.e., "If I press here and pull there, the sinuses will get better", our sense of the energy is diminished.

Working with energy will positively affect nerves, organs, muscles, and bones. However, we must learn to trust in our own energy model before we begin translating it into another. Dr. Stone warns us many times not to make the mistake of putting anatomy and physiology before energy.

Later protocols will relate more to Dr. Stone's specific treatments for sciatica, lower back pain, hemorrhoids, etc. We must remember that, regardless of Dr. Stone's anatomical reasoning, his treatments are always based on energy. Sometimes Dr. Stone will recreate an established chiropractic and osteopathic treatment from an energetic perspective. He then calls these treatments "old moves with a new emphasis." At other times, Dr. Stone just makes up new treatments from his experience of being with the energy. The majority of his treatment strategies relate back to his "weaving energy chart" (Bk I, Ch 5) which is the basis for the element protocols.

ETHER ELEMENT

VISUALIZATIONS FOR ETHER

Imagine sitting deep within a forest, feeling a profound sense of peace.

Imagine being in a huge open meadow with a clear blue sky above you.

Imagine an empty page ready for your idea.

Imagine the silence just after a great musical performance.

Imagine an openness in your throat and the ability to express yourself freely.

ETHER ELEMENT EXERCISE

Find a quiet, peaceful place. Sit very still for at least 10 minutes, allowing your thoughts to disappear. Let yourself to become calm. If a thought of something to do crosses your mind, let it go. Allow yourself to go into the silence.

When you open your eyes, what do you feel like inside?

What thoughts or associations come with this feeling? Does the feeling remind you of any past experiences or people you have known?

Are you aware of any emotions that come with this feeling?

What physical sensations do you perceive with this feeling? Describe these sensations and where they are located in your body.

Would you like more of this feeling? In what area of your life would you like more of this feeling?

Would you like to share this feeling with people close to you?

Do you have any value judgements associated with this feeling?

ETHER ELEMENT PROTOCOL

(Bk II Ch 33,59; Bk III Ch 4,5; Bk V Ch 12, Fig. 3,4) [BW: IV.E7a,b]

1. Cradle

2. Crown Spread

Right Side:

3. TMJ to Shoulder

4. Elbow to Knee

5. Wrist to Ankle

6. Thumb to Big Toe

7. Big Toe Cradle
   (both feet)

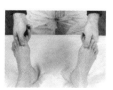

Left Side:

8. Big Toe to Thumb

9. Ankle to Wrist

10. Knee to Elbow

11. TMJ to Shoulder

12. Cradle

ETHER ELEMENT REFLEX AREAS

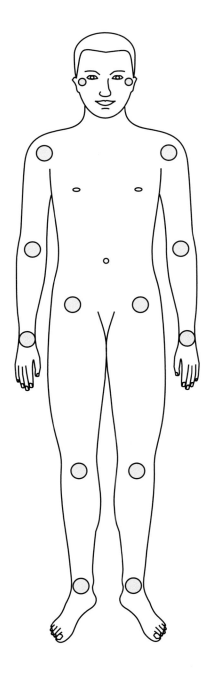

 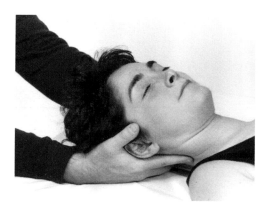

Cradle: Keep your hands soft and relaxed. The touch is satvic. Your index fingers go down the sides of the neck, your middle fingers cross at the occipital base, and your thumbs rest by the ears. The head should be entirely cradled in your hands and not touching the table.

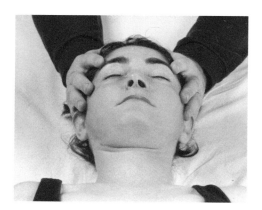 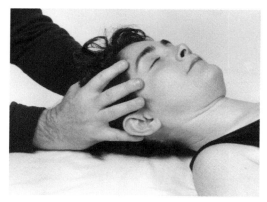

Crown Spread: Evenly spread your fingers around the head with your little fingers at the back of the ears (mastoid process), your ring fingers in front of the ears (TMJ), your middle fingers near the temples (sphenoid), your index fingers on the forehead (frontal), and your thumbs on the top of the head (parietal).

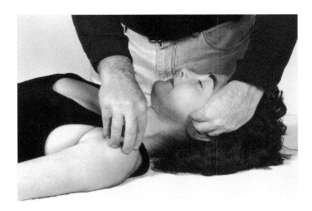

TMJ to Shoulder: *(Please note that the picture shows the move from the opposite side for clarity of placement. The move is done on the same side as you are standing without your hands crossing over the body.)* Place all five fingers or your thumb satvically on the TMJ and shoulder. Visualize space. You may also find resonant points in the auric field just off these areas of the body. Hold until you feel a unified pulse between your hands.

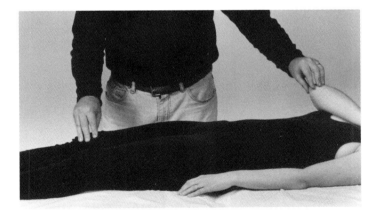

Elbow to Knee: *(Please note that the elbow is raised in the photo for clarity of placement. The move is done with the arm lying flat on the table.)* Place all five fingers or your thumb satvically on the elbow and knee. You may also find resonant points in the auric field just off these areas of the body. Hold until you feel a unified pulse between your hands.

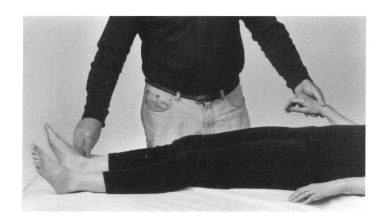

Wrist to Ankle: *(Please note that the wrist is raised in the photo for clarity of placement. The move is done with the wrist flat on the table.)* Place all five fingers or your thumb satvically on the wrist and ankle. You may also find resonant points in the auric field just off these areas of the body. Hold until you feel a unified pulse between your hands.

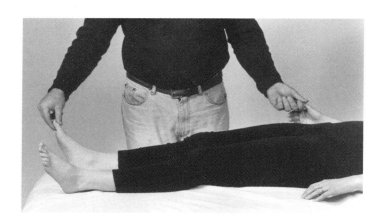

Thumb to Big Toe: Satvically hold the thumb and big toe between your thumb and first finger. Hold until you feel a unified pulse between your hands.

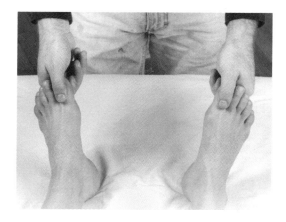

Big Toe Cradle: Satvically hold the big toes between your thumb and first finger. Hold until you feel a unified pulse between your hands.

ETHER ELEMENT EVALUATION

INQUIRY
[EV: 10a,b; 11a,b]

Do you experience space and freedom in your life?

Do you feel trapped?

Do you have fears around self-expression? In what areas of your life, e.g., work, relationships, etc?

Does your throat ever tighten or feel blocked when you express yourself or think about expressing yourself?

Do you have any spiritual pursuits?

Have you experienced any significant losses in your life, either recently or in the past?

Do you listen?

How are your sleeping patterns, e.g., restless, deep, sound?

Do you experience any joint pains?

OBSERVATION
[EV: 10c,d,e]

Check the visual appearance of the neck, e.g., is it stuck out, held back, thick, elongated?

Check for joint tightness/mobility. (Bk III Ch 4, 5) [EV: 9e]

Check the quality of the voice. (EES Ch 21) (*Music & Sound,* pp. 53-77) [EV: 9b2]
   + open/resonant/free flowing
   − tight/constricted/held back

Check for the ability to be still. (Bk V p. 60) [EV: 3]

Check for tissue elongation and/or excess flaccidity. [EV:10b]

Do you ever have difficulty swallowing? Does your throat get dry?

Check hair quality, e.g., oily, dry, thin, thick.

Notes

ETHER ELEMENT NOTES

General Qualities: Space, Freedom of Expression, Openness, Stillness—Air, Fire, Water, and Earth are created out of Ether. Ether is a mixing bowl for the four elements.

Sense: Hearing

Color: Blue

Emotions: + Return to Spirit
           – Grief

Body Structures (functions): Throat (expression), Joints (flexibility), Body Cavities (space), Ears (hearing/listening), Thyroid Gland (metabolism), Ultrasonic Core (meditation)

Gemstone: Moonstone

Sound: Silence

Seed Mantrum: HAM

Art: Music

AIR ELEMENT

AIR ELEMENT VISUALIZATIONS

Imagine feeling the wind moving and swirling in different directions.

Imagine being a child and wanting to do everything all at once.

Imagine having many ideas and seeing them all interconnected.

Imagine flying through the air.

Imagine a storyteller telling a story within a story within a story within a story...and they all seem to relate and make sense.

Imagine moving quickly, suddenly changing direction, then changing direction again and again.

AIR ELEMENT EXERCISE

Spend five minutes talking very fast, quickly move from one thing to another and skipping from topic to topic. Walk to the kitchen, start something, then walk to the living room, start something, then walk back to the kitchen. In between, think of something else you should be doing. Scratch your head fast. Open a window, then come back and close the window. Keep moving like this for five minutes. When five minutes are up, close your eyes.

What do you feel like inside?

What thoughts or associations come with this feeling? Does the feeling remind you of any past experiences or people you have known?

Are you aware of any emotions that come with this feeling?

What physical sensations do you perceive with this feeling? Describe these sensations and where they are located in your body.

Would you like more of this feeling? In what area of your life would you like more of this feeling?

Would you like to share this feeling with people close to you?

Do you have any value judgements associated with this feeling?

AIR ELEMENT PROTOCOL

(Bk V Ch 11) [BW: IV.E2]

1. Cradle

2. Gemini
   Shoulder Shake

3. Gemini/Libra
   Diaphragm Release
   (*right & left sides*)

4. Air Element
   Line Balance
   (*right & left sides*)

Right & Left Feet:

5.a. Aquarius
   Ankle Cradle

b. Lean and Pull

c. Aquarius
   Ankle Rotation

d. Brachial
   Plexus Reflex

e. Pull Air Toe

f. Work Air Tendon

Turn Client Over

6. Aquarius/Libra
   Circuit

7. Aquarius/Gemini
   Circuit

8. Libra Balance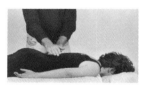

9. Libra/Gemini Circuit

10. Air Brushing

AIR ELEMENT ASTROLOGICAL REFLEX AREAS
Gemini/Libra/Aquarius

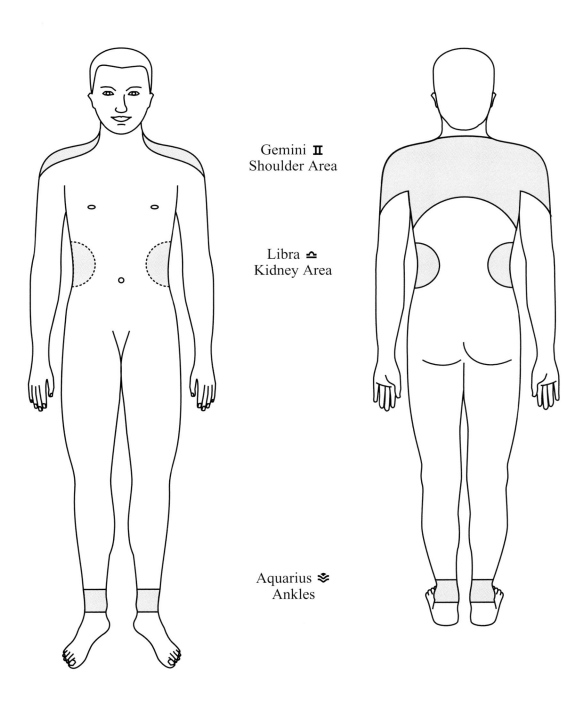

Gemini ♊
Shoulder Area

Libra ♎
Kidney Area

Aquarius ♒
Ankles

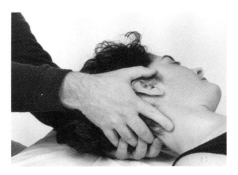 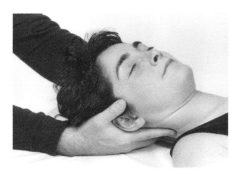

Cradle: Keep your hands soft and relaxed. The touch is satvic. Your index fingers go down the sides of the neck, your middle fingers cross at the occipital base, and your thumbs rest by the ears. The head should be entirely cradled in your hands and not touching the table.

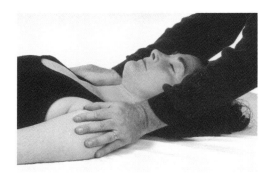

Gemini Shoulder Shake: Place your palms over the tops of the shoulders as shown. Allow yourself to resonate with the quality of "Gemini Air" while simultaneously rocking the shoulders back and forth. The rhythm and speed of the shaking can be adjusted based on how your client's body responds to your touch. In general, Air tends to move quickly.

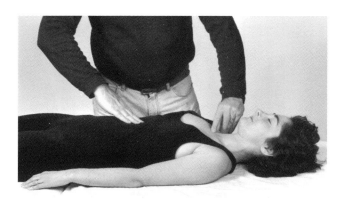

Gemini/Libra Diaphragm Release: (Bk IV Ch 8) Place your thumb or the tips of your fingers on the abdomen just below the rib cage as shown. The thumb and index finger of your other hand make contact with the head of the collar bone near the center of the neck and your fingers grip the body of the collar bone. As your client breathes in, rock the collar bone back and forth. As your client breathes out, press inward and rock with your fingers below the rib cage. Continue breathing and rocking, allowing both of your hands to move outward in unison from the center toward the side of the body (laterally). Ask your client to breathe deeply and notice which areas open to the breath and which areas are resisting. Do both sides.
Warning: Do not press directly on the xiphoid process, located below the sternum at the center of the body.
[BW: IV.E3c]

Air Element Line Balance: Satvically hold the head of the collar bone in one hand. Place your thumb or first finger of your other hand just below the rib cage on the Air element line. Hold the contacts until you feel a unified pulse between your hands. You may also make other contacts anywhere along the Air element line.

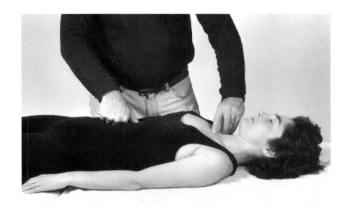

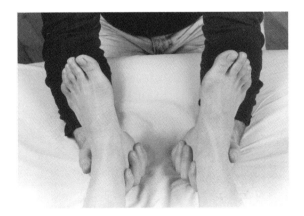

Aquarius Ankle Cradle: Satvically cradle the ankles in the palms of your hands as shown. Relax and tune into the energy.

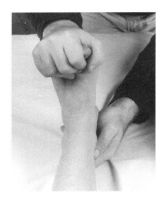
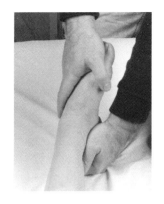

Lean and Pull: Rest the heel on the palm of one hand and grasp the ball of the foot with your other hand. Lean forward (superiorly) on the foot using your body weight to give the Achilles tendon a good stretch. Then place your hand over the center of the top of the foot and pull downward. The two movements should create a gentle pumping motion. Repeat several times.

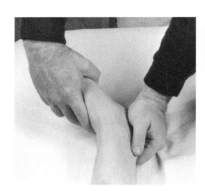

Aquarius Ankle Rotation: Hold the foot at the top of the ankle and twist it from side to side. Then stabilize the foot at the heel and rotate the foot in all directions. Do not force these moves. Start slowly to get a feel for your client's flexibility and gradually increase speed and pressure based on your client's response.

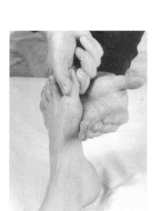
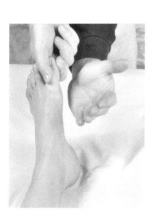

Brachial Plexus Reflex: Hold the big toe between your thumb and first finger and gently pull. Open your other hand as shown and "chop" with a moderate speed where the arch begins (just below the metatarsophalangeal joint). You should see a subtle ripple effect move up the entire body to the top of the head if the move is done correctly.

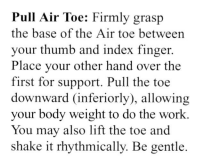
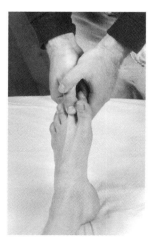

Pull Air Toe: Firmly grasp the base of the Air toe between your thumb and index finger. Place your other hand over the first for support. Pull the toe downward (inferiorly), allowing your body weight to do the work. You may also lift the toe and shake it rhythmically. Be gentle.

Work Air Tendon: With the thumb and index finger of one hand, grasp the Air toe, stretching it upward and back (superiorly). With the thumb of the other hand, "walk up" the Air tendon from the heel to the base of the toe. Feel free to pause and give extra attention to sore spots.

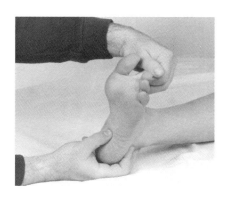

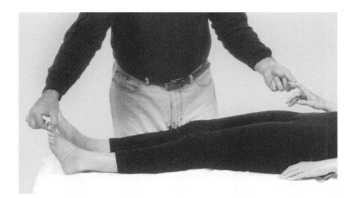

Air Balancing: Satvically hold the Air finger and Air toe until you feel a unified pulse between your hands.

Aquarius/Libra Circuit: (Bk V Ch 11) Place one of your hands either on or just above the ankles and your other hand on or over the kidney area until you feel a unified pulse between your hands. This may be done with your client lying face up or face down. You may also press the kidney reflex area of the foot with one hand and with your other hand, contact a sore spot in the area of the 11th or 12th thoracic verbebrae; make a circuit and hold until you feel a unified pulse between your hands.

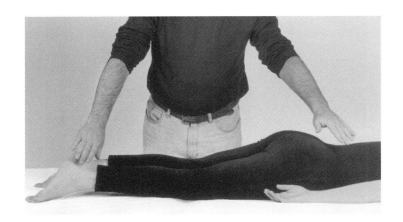

Aquarius/Gemini Circuit:
Hold one hand above the ankle or calf and your other hand over the shoulder. This may be done on a diagonal or the same side of the body. Hold until you feel a unified pulse between your hands.

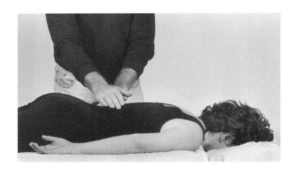

Libra Balance: Hold both hands above the kidneys as shown and tune into the energy. Hold until you feel a unified pulse between your hands.

Back View

Front View

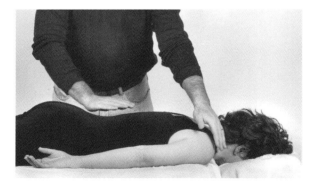

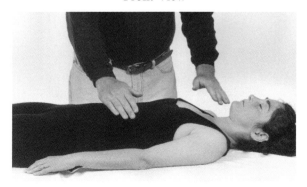

Libra/Gemini Circuit: Hold one hand over the kidney area and your other hand over the shoulder, on or just off the body. The move may be done either on a diagonal or on the same side of the body. It may also be done with your client lying face up or face down. Hold until you feel a unified pulse between your hands.

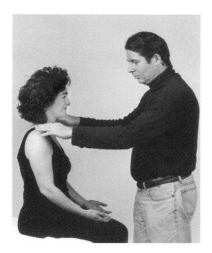

Air Brushing: Begin with both hands at the shoulders. Your client's palms should be facing upward. Quickly and lightly sweep down the arms and over the palms, lifting your hands upward at the end of the sweep. Do this several times with a light, airy feeling.

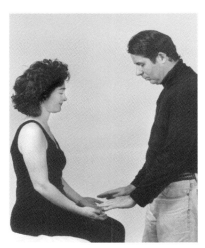

AIR ELEMENT EVALUATION

INQUIRY
[EV: 10a,b; 11a,b]

Do you think and move quickly?

Are you involved in many projects at once, running from one to the next?

Do you feel as if your life is moving very fast?

Do you feel grounded?

Do you feel scattered?

Do you solve problems quickly?

Do you think a lot?

Do you get impatient a lot?

Do you have needs and desires that you feel are not met?

OBSERVATION
[EV: 10c,d,e]

Check the visual appearance of the shoulders, ankles, and chest. Is the chest caved in? Are the shoulders uneven? Are the ankles too thin to support the body?

Does your client move quickly? Are they all over the place? Do they ever slow down?

Does your client talk constantly?

Check the quality of the voice. (EES Ch 21)
(*Music & Sound,* pp. 53-77) [EV: 9b2]
+ fast
– scattered/jumpy/breathy

Do you get thirsty easily? How much water do you drink?

Check skin for dryness, rashes, redness, roughness, itchy areas, scaliness.

Check pores and ability of skin to eliminate.

Notes

AIR ELEMENT NOTES

General Qualities: Airiness, Mobility, Gentleness, Lightness, Quickness

Sense: Touch

Color: Green

Emotions: + Compassion/Charity/Unconditional Love
       – Desire/Bargaining/Passing Judgment

Body Structures (functions): Nervous System (mental activity, thought), Chest Cavity, Skin, Lungs (breathing), Thymus Gland (immune response)

Astrological Reflex Areas: Shoulders, Mid-Back/Kidney, Calves & Ankles

Body Type: Ectomorphic—thin, wiry, underweight

Tissue Response: Speed of tissue response

Foods: Foods growing 6 feet or more above ground, e.g. fruits, nuts, seeds
       Green foods

Taste: Sour

Gemstone: Emerald

Sound: High-pitched, Fast

Seed Mantrum: YAM

Art: Dance

Notes

FIRE ELEMENT

FIRE ELEMENT VISUALIZATIONS

Imagine a blazing campfire with sparks rising into the night and disappearing.

Imagine being inside on a cold winter evening, sitting by a warm fire and gazing into the hot embers.

Imagine a quick burst of energy.

Imagine a volcano erupting.

Imagine being on the surface of the sun.

Imagine the head of a match bursting into flame.

Remember an excitement you couldn't contain.

FIRE ELEMENT EXERCISE

For the next five minutes speak with a loud, sharp, staccato voice while moving with sudden bursts of energy. Be excited and say as loud as you can, "I have a lot of Fire!" Do this several times. Really get into it. Let yourself go. Be safe and experience your fire. After five minutes, close your eyes.

What do you feel like inside?

What thoughts or associations come with this feeling? Does the feeling remind you of any past experiences or people you have known?

Are you aware of any emotions that come with this feeling?

What physical sensations do you perceive with this feeling? Describe these sensations and where they are located in your body.

Would you like more of this feeling? In what area of your life would you like more of this feeling?

Would you like to share this feeling with people close to you?

Do you have any value judgements associated with this feeling?

FIRE ELEMENT PROTOCOL

(Bk III Ch 4) [BW: IV.E4A]

1. Fire Cradle

2. Aries North Pole Stretch

3. Aries Fire Rub

4. Fire Element Line Circuit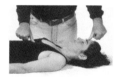

Left Side:

5. Chin/Navel Fire Circuit

6. Leo/Sagittarius Circuit on Fire Element Line

7. Sagittarius Rock

8. Leo/Sagittarius Balance

9. Aries/Sagittarius Balance

10. Pull Fire Toe

11. Work Fire Tendon

Right Side:

12. Pull Fire Toe

13. Work Fire Tendon

14. Sagittarius Rock

15. Leo/Sagittarius Circuit on Fire Element Line

16. Chin/Navel Fire Circuit

17. Fire Element Line Circuit

18. Aries Fire Balance

FIRE ELEMENT ASTROLOGICAL REFLEX AREAS
Aries/Leo/Sagittarius

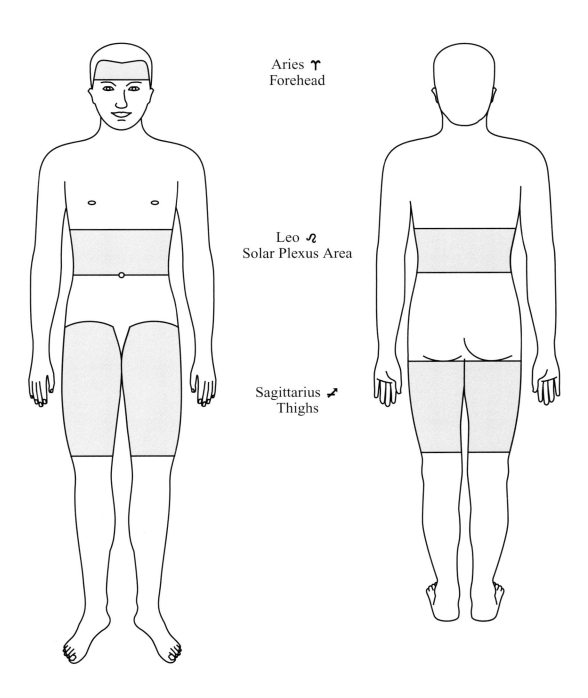

Aries ♈
Forehead

Leo ♌
Solar Plexus Area

Sagittarius ♐
Thighs

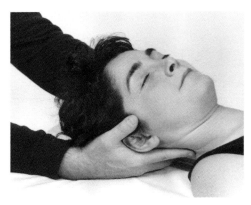

Fire Cradle: Keep your hands soft and relaxed. The touch is satvic. Your index fingers go down the sides of the neck, your middle fingers cross at the occipital base, and your thumbs rest by the ears. The head should be entirely cradled in your hands and not touching the table. Imagine sending a warm, fiery energy down the vagus nerve (which exits the skull just below the ear and runs down along the side of the neck).

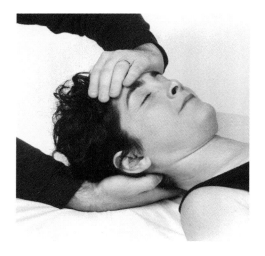

Aries North Pole Stretch: Rest the head on the palm of your right hand and lightly grasp the occipital base on either side of the cervical spine on the Fire element line with your middle finger and thumb. Place your left hand on the forehead with a feeling of upward movement. Tune into "Aries Fire" as you apply a steady, light traction with your right hand.

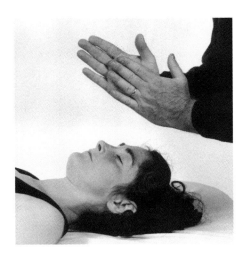

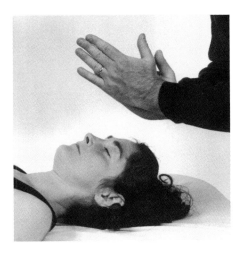

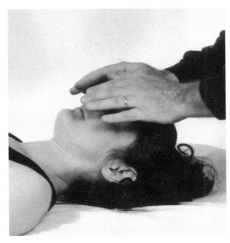

Aries Fire Rub: Vigorously rub your hands together as shown. Place the center of your palms over the eyes and hold until the heat is absorbed from your hands. Lift off gradually.

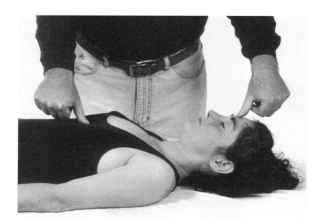

Aries/Leo Circuit on Fire Element Line: Place your left thumb on the forehead just above the center of the eye and your right thumb on the Fire element line just below the rib cage. Hold until you feel a unified pulse between your hands.

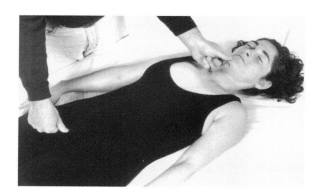

Chin/Navel Fire Circuit: Place your left thumb and forefinger on the mandible or jaw along the Fire element line. Place your right thumb on the navel. Hold until you feel a unified pulse between your hands.

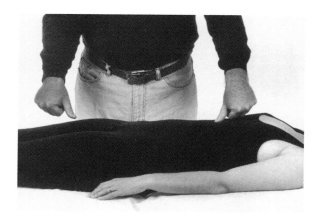

Leo/Sagittarius Circuit on Fire Element Line: Place your left thumb on the Fire element line just below the rib cage and your right thumb anywhere along the Fire element line on the center of the thigh. Hold until you feel a unified pulse between your hands.

Sagittarius Rock: Place one hand approximately one inch to the side of the navel. Hold the thigh in the palm of your other hand as shown and rock it back and forth. Pause occasionally to feel the energy, then resume rocking.

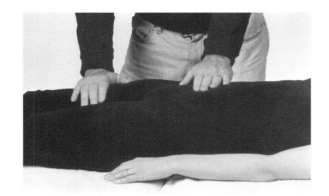

Leo/Sagittarius Balance: Hold one hand above the solar plexus and your other hand above the thigh approximately one to three inches above the body. Hold until your feel a unified pulse between your hands.Or you may rapidly brush towards the feet with your bottom hand. Feel free to make fiery sounds. You can try making the sound of the Fire Mantra RAM.

Aries/Sagittarius Balance: Hold one hand above the forehead and your other hand above the thigh approximately one to three inches above the body. Hold until you feel a unified pulse between your hands.

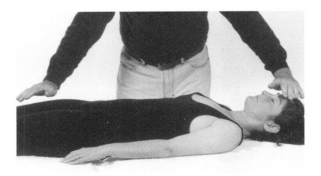

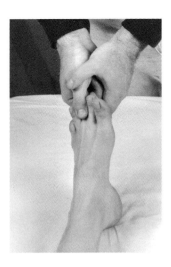

Pull Fire Toe: Grasp the base of the Fire toe between your thumb and index finger. Place your other hand over the first for support. Pull the toe downward (inferiorly), allowing your body weight to do the work. You may also lift the toe and shake it rhythmically. Be gentle.

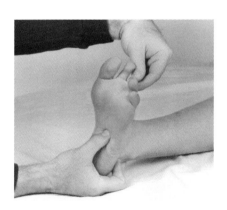

Work Fire Tendon: With the thumb and index finger of one hand, grasp the Fire toe, stretching it upward and back (superiorly). With the thumb of the other hand, "walk up" the Fire tendon from the heel to the base of the toe. Feel free to pause and give extra attention to sore spots. With Fire you may want to ask your client to make sounds, drawing Fire energy upward toward their throat.

Aries Fire Balance: Hold your hands between one and three inches above the forehead for thirty seconds to a minute. Gradually lift your hands upward and away from the body.

FIRE ELEMENT EVALUATION

INQUIRY

[EV: 10a,b; 11a,b]

Do you take quick and direct action to get the things you want?

Are you enthusiastic?

Can you get angry?

Do you get angry a lot?

Do you begin projects with a "bang" and then fizzle out?

Would you describe yourself as a leader?

Do you harbor resentments towards people in your life?

Do you hold back anger, then explode?

Do you feel motivated?

How is your appetite? Your digestion?

Do you urinate frequently or infrequently?

OBSERVATION

[EV: 10c,d,e]

Check the visual appearance of the solar plexus for contraction or expansion.

Check the eyes for brightness.

Check the voice for loudness and clarity.

Check the proportion of the thighs in relation to the rest of the body.

Check the quality of the voice. (EES Ch 21)
(*Music & Sound,* pp. 53-77) [EV: 9b2]
    + sharp/clear/staccato
    – loud/overbearing

Check the speed of the pulse and blood pressure.

Check for tissue inflammation, e.g., ulcers, boils, varicose veins.

Notes

FIRE ELEMENT NOTES

General Qualities: Heat, Brightness, Upward Movement, Clarity, Warmth
Expansiveness, Radiating Outward

Sense: Sight

Color: Yellow

Emotions: + Forgiveness/Enthusiasm
– Anger/Resentment

Body Structures (functions): Stomach, Liver, Pancreas, Spleen, Gallbladder (digestion);
Heart (circulation); Adrenal Glands (stress response)

Astrological Reflex Areas: Forehead, Solar Plexus, Thighs

Body Type: Mesomorphic—muscular, perfectly proportioned, athletic, medium build

Tissue Response: Shaking

Foods: Foods growing 2 feet to 6 feet above the ground, e.g. grains, legumes, sunflower/sesame seeds
Yellow foods

Taste: Bitter

Gemstone: Coral

Sound: Loud and Staccato

Seed Mantrum: RAM

Art: Painting

WATER ELEMENT

WATER ELEMENT VISUALIZATIONS

Imagine a dancer moving gracefully with flowing movements.

Listen to a Chopin Nocturne.

Imagine sitting by a stream, listening to the flowing water.

Imagine floating in the ocean, feeling the waves rise and fall.

Imagine a cool drink of fresh water on a hot day.

Remember a time when you had a creative idea.

Imagine a dolphin swimming through the ocean, moving in the currents.

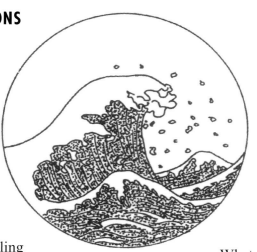

WATER ELEMENT WORKBOOK

Let your body move and flow, so all your movements feel connected. Everything you do connects to everything else. Let one movement lead to the next without stopping. Even when you speak, let your words flow and connect. Do this for five minutes, then close your eyes.

What do you feel like inside?

What thoughts or associations come with this feeling? Does the feeling remind you of any past experiences or people you have known?

Are you aware of any emotions that come with this feeling?

What physical sensations do you perceive with this feeling? Describe these sensations and where they are located in your body.

Would you like more of this feeling? In what area of your life would you like more of this feeling?

Would you like to share this feeling with people close to you?

Do you have any value judgements associated with this feeling?

WATER ELEMENT PROTOCOL

(Bk V Ch 11) [BW: IV.E2]

1. Water Cradle

2. Tummy Rock

3. Cancer/Scorpio
   Balance

4. Pisces/Scorpio
   Diagonal Balance
   (left to right)

5. Pisces/Cancer
   Diagonal Balance
   (left to right)

Right & Left Feet:

6. Pisces Foot Pump

7. Pull Water Toe

8. Work Water
   Tendon

9. Pisces/Scorpio
   Diagonal Balance
   (right to left)

10. Pisces/Cancer
    Diagonal Balance
    (right to left)

Turn Client Over

11. Pisces/Scorpio
    Water Pump
    (right & left sides)

12. Scorpio/Cancer
    Diagonal Circuit
    (right & left sides)

13. Cancer
    Shoulder Rub

14. Cancer
    Water Balance

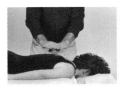

WATER ELEMENT ASTROLOGICAL REFLEX AREAS

Cancer/Scorpio/Pisces

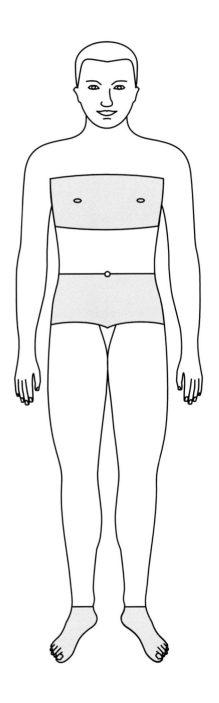
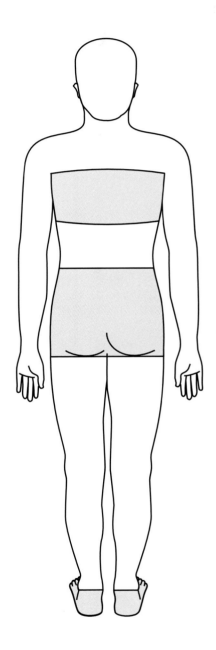

Cancer ♋
Breast Area

Scorpio ♏
Pelvic Area

Pisces ♓
Feet

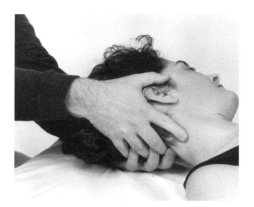
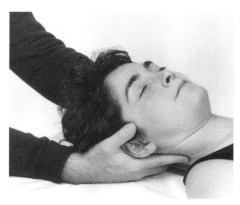

Water Cradle: Keep your hands soft and relaxed. The touch is satvic. Your index fingers go down the sides of the neck, your middle fingers cross at the occipital base, and your thumbs rest by the ears. The head should be entirely cradled in your hands and not touching the table.

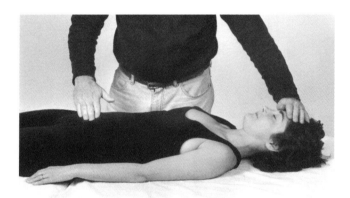

Tummy Rock Rest your left hand gently on the forehead and your right hand about 1½" below the navel. With your right hand rock rhythmically (rajas). Stop and feel the energy (satvas).

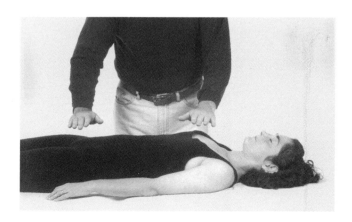

Cancer/Scorpio Balance: Hold your left hand two to four inches above the breast bone (sternum) and your right hand two to four inches above the pubic bone. Hold until you feel a unified pulse between your hands.

Pisces/Scorpio Diagonal Balance: Hold your left hand one to three inches above the pubic bone and your right hand on the bottom of the left foot. Hold until you feel a unified pulse between your hands.

Pisces/Cancer Diagonal Balance: Hold your left hand one to three inches above the breast bone (sternum) and your right hand on the bottom of the left foot. Hold until you feel a unified pulse between your hands.

Pisces Foot Pump: Rest the heel on the palm of one hand and grasp the ball of the foot with your other hand. Lean forward (superiorly) on the foot using your body weight to give the Achilles tendon a good stretch. Then place your hand over the center of the top of the foot and pull downward. The two movements should create a gentle pumping motion. Repeat several times on each foot with a "Watery" rhythm.

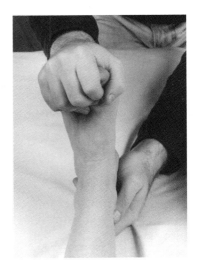
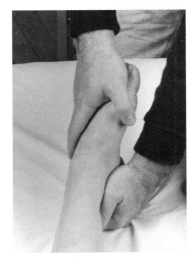

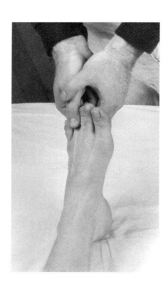

Pull Water Toe: Grasp the base of the Water toe between your thumb and index finger. Place your other hand over the first for support. Pull the toe downward (inferiorly), allowing your body weight to do the work. You may also lift the toe and shake it rhythmically. Be gentle.

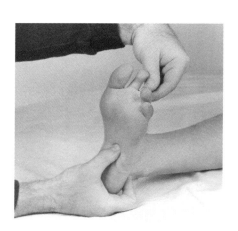

Work Water Tendon: With the thumb and index finger of one hand, grasp the Water toe, stretching it upward and back (superiorly). With the thumb of the other hand, "walk up" the Water tendon from the heel to the base of the toe. Feel free to pause and give extra attention to sore spots.

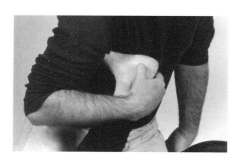  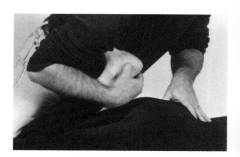

Pisces/Scorpio Water Pump: With client face down, hold the foot securely underneath one of your arms as shown. Find a sensitive point on the outer ankle and press into it with your middle finger as you move the foot toward the buttocks (superiorly), flexing the knee. Then straighten the leg while pressing into a sensitive point near the center of the hip with the thumb of your other hand. Do this three to ten times, varying the pumping rhythm.

Scorpio/Cancer Diagonal Circuit:
Place one of your hands at the center of the
buttocks and your other hand over the area
between the shoulder blades creating a
diagonal as shown. "Ping pong" between
the two points until you feel a unified pulse.

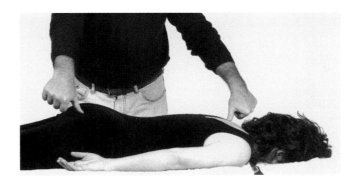

Cancer Shoulder Rub: Place your
hands over the shoulder blades and
press downward in clockwise circles.
Project a feeling of comfort and
nurturing.

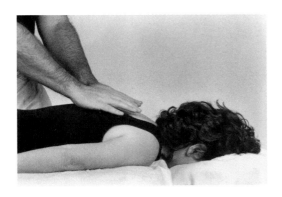

Cancer Water Balance: Cross
both hands above the center of the
shoulder blades, one to three
inches above the body. Hold for
approximately one minute, then
lift your hands slowly upward and
away from the body.

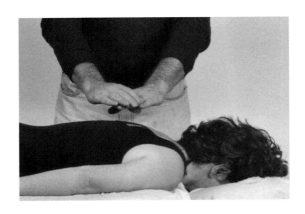

WATER ELEMENT EVALUATION

INQUIRY

[EV: 10a,b; 11a,b]

How are your relationships?

Are you able to go with the flow?

Do you have any creative outlets?

Do you ever feel out of touch with your feelings?

Do you ever get overwhelmed by your feelings?

Do you get attached to people and have difficulty letting go?

How do you feel about yourself sexually? Is your sex drive low, medium or high?

Do you ever feel bloated, puffy or water-logged?

OBSERVATION

[EV: 10c,d,e]

Check the proportional relationships of the breasts, hips, and feet to the rest of the body.

Check for swelling, bloating, and water retention.

Check body movements for flowing qualities and/or disconnections?

Check the quality of the voice (EES Ch 21) (*Music & Sound,* pp. 53-77) [EV: 9b2]:
+ rhythmic/flowing/smooth
− ongoing, connected talking/babbling

Check luster of skin, e.g., glowing, radiant, dull, pasty.

Check hair quality, e.g., oily, dry, thin, thick.

Notes

WATER ELEMENT NOTES

General Qualities: Fluidity, Smoothness, Ripeness, Flowing, Watery, Nurturing, Mothering

Sense: Taste

Color: Orange

Emotions: + Letting go
— Attachment

Body Structures (functions): Generative Organs (reproduction), Breasts, Lymphatic System (cleansing), Secretory Glands, Bladder, Ovaries

Astrological Reflex Areas: Breasts, Pelvis, Feet

Body Type: Endomorphic—fully developed, possibly overweight

Tissue Response: Flowing Movement

Foods: Foods growing from ground level to 2 feet, e.g. green vegetables, melons, cucumbers, squash Orange Foods

Taste: Salty

Gemstone: Pearl

Sound: Smooth and flowing

Seed Mantrum: VAM

Art: Cuisine, Cooking

Notes

EARTH ELEMENT

EARTH ELEMENT VISUALIZATIONS

Imagine cows grazing in a field, moving very slowly.

Imagine a deep feeling of security.

Imagine a farmer with a thick neck and big work-worn hands, walking slowly through a corn field on a warm summer day.

Imagine feeling warm earth in your hands and squeezing it between your fingers.

Imagine slowly sliding into a warm mud bath.

Imagine someone speaking to you in a deep, slow, calm voice.

Think slowly and take your time.

EARTH ELEMENT EXERCISE

For five minutes move in slow motion. Talk slowly. Walk slowly. Feel your feet on the floor. Breathe deeply. Slow yourself down. Do this for at least ten or fifteen minutes and then close your eyes.

What do you feel like inside?

What thoughts or associations come with this feeling? Does the feeling remind you of any past experiences or people you have known?

Are you aware of any emotions that come with this feeling?

What physical sensations do you perceive with this feeling? Describe these sensations and where they are located in your body.

Would you like more of this feeling? In what area of your life would you like more of this feeling?

Would you like to share this feeling with people close to you?

Do you have any value judgements associated with this feeling?

EARTH ELEMENT PROTOCOL

[BW: IV.E5]

1. Earth Cradle

2. Taurus Neck Rub

3. Taurus Neck Stretch

4. Taurus/Virgo Balance
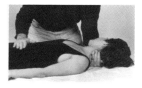

Right Side:

5. Virgo/Capricorn
   Colon Reflex

6. Capricorn Balance

7. Work Earth Tendon

Left Side:

8. Work Earth Tendon

9. Virgo/Capricorn
   Colon Reflex

10. Capricorn Balance

11. Virgo Balance

12. Taurus/Capricorn
    Balance

13. Earth Brushing

EARTH ELEMENT ASTROLOGICAL REFLEX AREAS
Taurus/Virgo/Capricorn

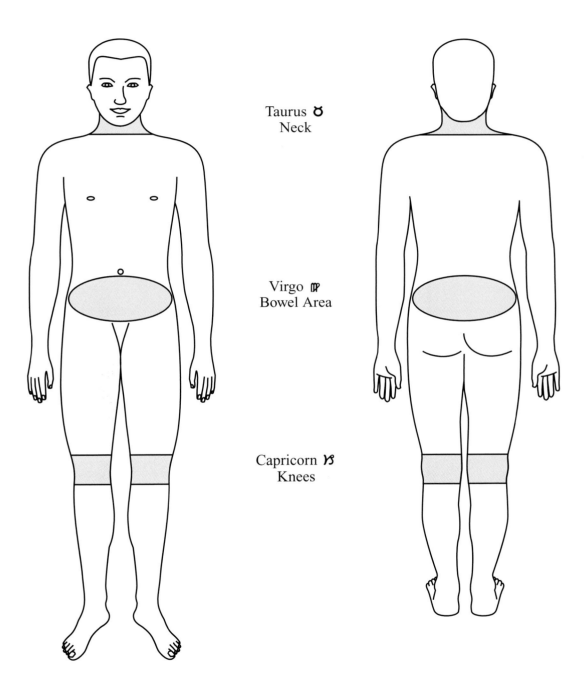

Taurus ♉
Neck

Virgo ♍
Bowel Area

Capricorn ♑
Knees

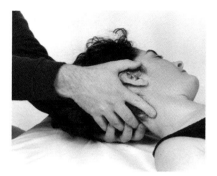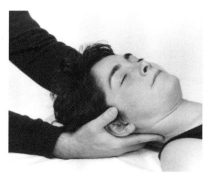

Earth Cradle: Keep your hands soft and relaxed. The touch is satvic. Your index fingers go down the sides of the neck, your middle fingers cross at the occipital base, and your thumbs rest by the ears. The head should be entirely cradled in your hands and not touching the table. Project a feeling of earthy security through your hands. Let your client know non-verbally that they are being held by Mother Earth and that everything is safe.

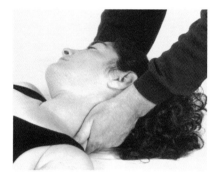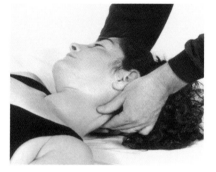

Taurus Neck Rub: Securely hold the neck in both hands. Tune into the quality of "Taurus Earth" and let your client know with your hands that their neck is secure and everything is okay. Then gently and slowly knead the trapezius and scalene muscles.

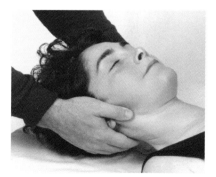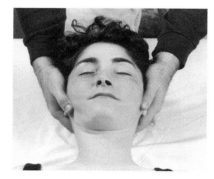

Taurus Neck Stretch: Hold the neck firmly and securely at the occipital base as shown and gently apply superior traction.

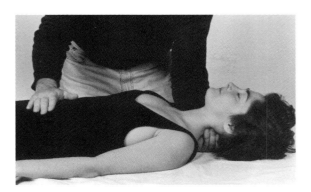 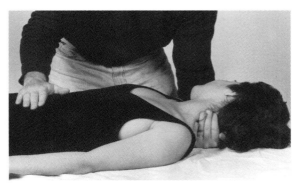

Taurus/Virgo Balance: Hold the back of the neck in the palm of your left hand as shown and place your right hand satvically over the lower abdomen approximately one inch above the pubic bone. Project a sense of earthy security through your hands and hold until you feel a unified pulse between your hands. Feel free to hold this for several minutes. You can also make an energy circuit by placing your left index finger on a tender spot on the back of the neck in the area of C3-5 and your right index finger on a tender spot along the side of the spine in the area between T12-L2. *See diagram.*

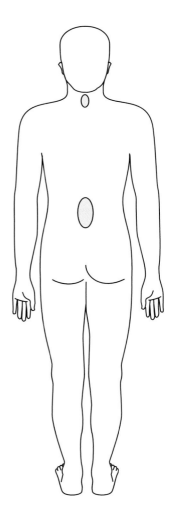

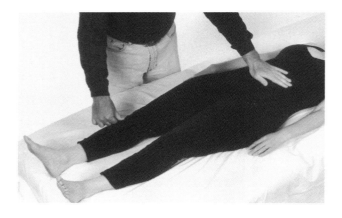

Virgo/Capricorn Colon Reflex: (Bk II Ch 60) Place your left hand over the lower abdomen one to two inches above the pubis. Place your right thumb on the Earth element line, on the soft tissue just above the outer ankle of the right leg. Work your way up to the knee. Then, place your right hand over the lower abdomen and your left thumb on the Earth element line just below the left knee. Work your way down to the ankle. You may also want to make an energy circuit by holding a tender spot along the side of the spine in the area between T12-L2 and another tender spot on the back of the knee. Hold until you feel a unified pulse between your hands. *See diagram.*

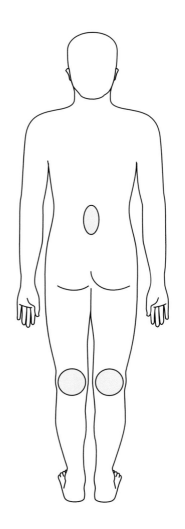

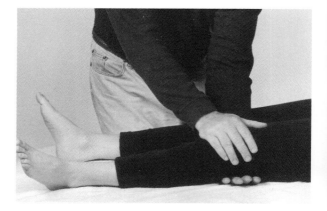

Capricorn Balance: Hold the knee between your hands with a steady, satvic touch.

Work Earth Tendon: With the thumb and index finger of one hand, grasp the Earth toe, stretching it upward and back (superiorly). With the thumb of the other hand, "walk up" the Earth tendon from the heel to the base of the toe. Feel free to pause and give extra attention to sore spots.

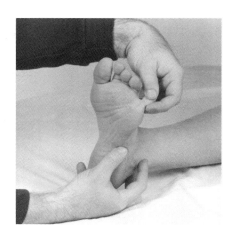

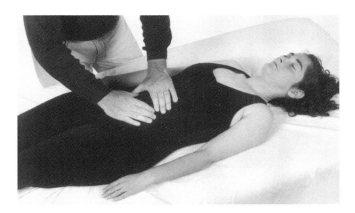

Virgo Balance: Place both hands over the lower abdomen as shown. Hold with a steady, satvic pressure.

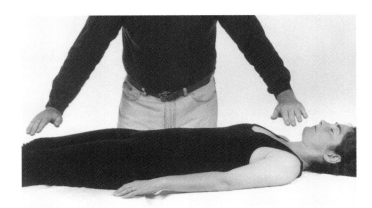

Taurus/Capricorn Balance: *(This may be done from the left or right side.)* Hold one hand over the neck and your other hand over the knees. When the distance "feels right," then that is the correct distance. Hold until you feel a unified pulse between your hands.

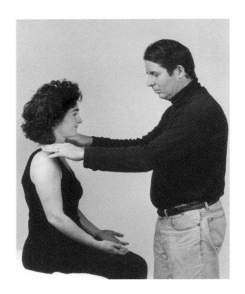

Earth Brushing: Begin with both hands at the shoulders. Your client's palms should be facing upwards. With a secure pressure, move slowly down the arms and over the palms. Do this several times.

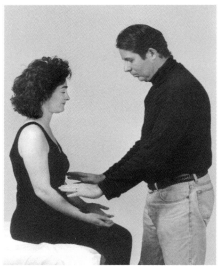

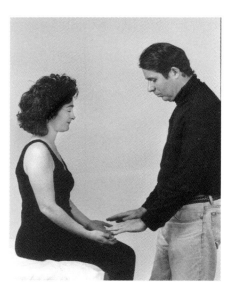

EARTH ELEMENT EVALUATION

INQUIRY
[EV: 10a,b; 11a,b]

Are you organized and structured?

Do you have patience with yourself and others?

Are you possessive about people and things?

Do you feel safe and secure?

Do you handle your finances well?

Are you fearful?

Are you able to establish secure boundaries with people?

Do you feel contracted or pushed in?

Do you feel lazy or as though you are stuck, unable to move?

Do you experience lower back, neck or knee problems?

Do you experience colon problems?

OBSERVATION
[EV: 10c,d,e]

Check the visual appearance of the neck, lower abdomen (bowel area), and knees.

Palpate for tissue rigidity in lower back, abdomen, and knees.

Is body movement slow?

Check the quality of the voice (EES Ch 21)
(*Music & Sound*, pp. 53-77) [EV: 9b2]:
    + low/deep/resonant/slow/steady
    − tight/constricted

Check for cold hands and feet.

Check bone size.

Notes

EARTH ELEMENT NOTES

General Qualities: Slow, Steady, Secure, Grounded, Structured, Crystalized, Organized

Sense: Smell

Color: Red

Emotions: + Courage
            – Fear

Body Structures (functions): Bones (structure, stability), Colon (elimination), Testes (reproduction)

Astrological Reflex Areas: Neck, Bowels, Knees

Body Type: Endomorphic—Stout, strong, thick neck, farmer-like

Tissue Response: Contraction

Foods: Foods growing below ground, e.g., root vegetables, tubers, beets, potatoes, carrots, onions

Taste: Sweet

Gemstone: Ruby

Sound: Low, Deep, Droning, Slow

Seed Mantrum: LAM

Art: Aromatherapy, Sculpture

ELEMENT THEORY NOTES

HUMAN ENERGY DYNAMICS

(Bk II Ch 1,2,3) [TH: I.A,B,C]

Ultrasonic Core: This is the current of the Air Principle. It is the primary energy which builds and sustains all others. It is sometimes referred to as our soul, our fundamental tone, our Spirit, or our inner Sound. Dr. Stone describes the energy of the ultrasonic core in many different ways. You may find him referring to it as Satvic, Neutral, East-West Energy Currents, Primary Life Current, core of our being, Sushunma, and the trunk of the Tree of Life. He even calls it the chimney that Santa Claus slides down.

Positive Current: This is the current of the Fire Principle. Dr. Stone calls it by different names depending upon the context in which it is being used: Yang, Rajas, Fire Principle, Positive Current, male, involution, sun, gold, Pignala, and Spiral Energy Current. The positive outflow of this energy from the ultrasonic core creates the oval fields.

Negative Current: This is the current of the Water Principle. Dr. Stone calls it by different names depending upon the context in which he is using it: Yin, Tamas, Water Principle, Negative Current, evolution, moon, silver, Ida, and Long Line Energy Currents. The negative return flow of this energy to the Ultrasonic Core creates the chakras.

The three currents are symbolized by the ancient symbol of the Caduceus. (Bk I Ch 1)

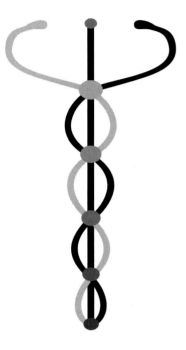

THE FIVE OVAL FIELDS

(Bk II Ch 1) (*Polarity Process,* pp. 29-30/38-44)
[TH: III.C,D]

A basic knowledge of the formation of the oval fields is necessary to understand the importance of their relationship with the chakras. Imagine the oval fields as empty spaces with boundaries, e.g., an empty bottle, a room without furniture, a tennis court without players, etc. Each space has a certain shape and quality. In the physical body, the oval fields are cavities surrounded by fascia and bone. The oval fields are given elemental names, i.e., Ether, Air, Fire, Water, and Earth. These names represent spacial qualities. They do not represent the elemental expression of the chakras.

The oval fields are structural and are created our of the six-pointed star or masculine principle. They provide the structure through which the elements can express themselves. To understand this principle imagine a musician playing a piano. The musician playing the piano represents the expressive energy of the chakras. The piano is the structure. The musician and piano together represent the expressive energy of the chakras. When the piano is in tune and working correctly, the musician can play beautiful music. The musician and piano together represent the proper relationship of structure (oval fields) to expression (elements/chakras). See the Structural Alignment Protocols for the practical application of Polarity Therapy for the structural alignment of the oval fields.

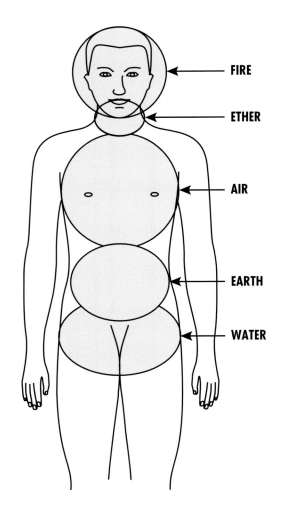

ASTROLOGICAL SIGNS & SYMBOLS REFERENCE

(Bk I pp. 48-53) (*Astrology & Elements,* pp. 71-110) [TH: III.G2]

Fire

♈ Aries: the beginning; bursting through; the Ram butting forward; fire igniting

♌ Leo: the Lion King; bright, sustained fire of the sun

♐ Sagittarius: shooting fire; a match igniting something; giving fire to another

Earth

♉ Taurus: secure, warm, sensuous earth; strong like a Bull

♍ Virgo: everything has a place; order; perfection; service

♑ Capricorn: structured earth; making connections; determination

Air

♊ Gemini: quick, light air; moving in different directions at once; immediate communication

♎ Libra: balance; justice; harmonizing opposites

♒ Aquarius: networks; information; social consciousness and coordination

Water

♋ Cancer: mothering; nurturing; home; protective

♏ Scorpio: deep, penetrating water; fearless; looks deep into darkness

♓ Pisces: the end; looking into the bottom of the ocean; compassion for suffering

THE FIVE ELEMENTS

(Bk II Ch 2) (*Polarity Process,* pp. 49-91) [TH: III.C; V.C]

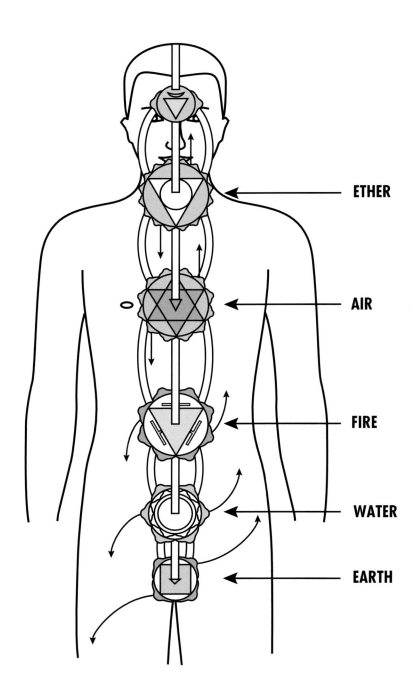

ETHER

AIR

FIRE

WATER

EARTH

ULTRASONIC CORE, CADUCEUS, AND FIVE CHAKRAS

ENERGY CURRENTS

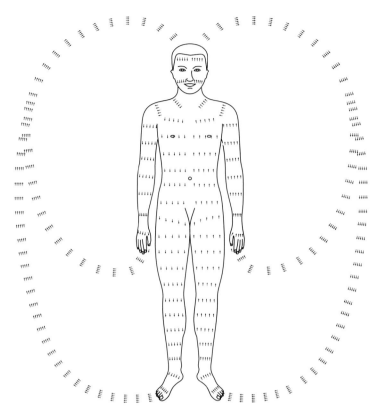

**NORTH-SOUTH ENERGY CURRENTS
(LONG LINE CURRENTS)**

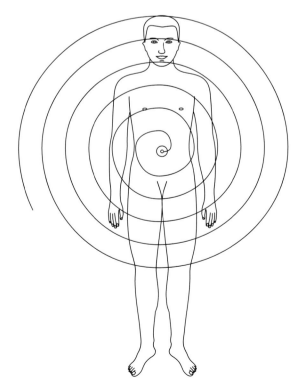

SPIRAL CURRENTS

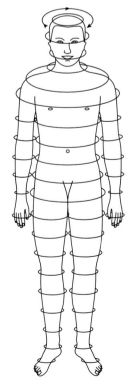

EAST-WEST ENERGY CURRENTS

Notes

REFLEXOLOGY PROTOCOL INTRODUCTION

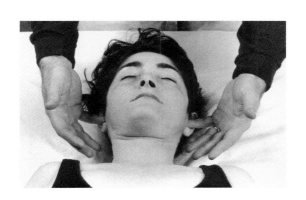

Understanding and working with reflexes is integral to the practice of Polarity Therapy. The reflexology protocols use foot, hand, and ear reflexes as a vehicle for understanding the principles of Polarity reflexology. They do not, by any means, cover all Polarity reflexes. The ear, hand, and foot have been chosen because of Dr. Stone's emphasis on the importance of these areas.

The mapping of reflexes used in Polarity reflexology is based on both energy flow patterns and corresponding anatomical relationships. The north-south elemental energy lines create the five longitudinal divisions of Ether, Air, Fire, Water, and Earth (Bk II Ch 3, 5, 6, 7) [TH: III.F]. In general, making contact along these lines in the direction of energy flow stimulates the associated elements, while pressing against the energy flow has the opposite effect and will sedate the associated element (Bk II Ch 23, 24) [BW: I.A1,2]. The elemental energy lines are continuous from front to back. Pressing anywhere along a line stimulates or sedates the whole line.

These anatomical relationships are based on the Hermetic principle of correspondence which states, "As above, so below." For example, the two feet, when put together, can be seen as the whole body (Bk V Ch 19). Looking at the feet in this way, we are able to create a miniature map of the physical body on the bottoms of the feet, complete with organs, glands, skeletal system, etc.

When north-south energy lines and anatomical correspondences are combined, we can press a specific point on the foot and have a corresponding effect via the energy line. This will then have a resonant effect at the anatomical target area.

Always remember that learning the "map" is only the first step in learning reflexology. Maps are not magical. They are only as effective as the practitioner's intention and quality of touch.

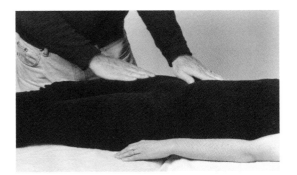

Sedating Contact Against Flow

FOOT REFLEXOLOGY PROTOCOL

1. Foot Cradle

2. Lymphatic Foot Pump

3. Ankle Rotation and Sidebending

4. Knuckle Rub

5. North Pole Stretch

6. Element Thumb Walk
   (bottom of foot)

7. Element Toe Pulls with Superior Tendon Walk and Element Toe Pulls
   (top of foot)

8. Balance Spinal Reflexes

9. Big Toe Adjustment

10. Arch Adjustments through Cuboid

11. Balance Head/Sinus Reflexes

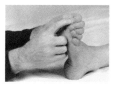

12. Balance Heart/Lung/ Respiratory Diaphragm Reflexes

13. Balance Digestive System Reflexes

14. Balance Kidney/ Adrenal Reflexes

15. Balance Large Intestine/Small Intestine Reflexes

16. Inside/Outside Heel Press

17. Balance Sciatic
    Reflexes

18. Balance Lymphatic
    Reflexes

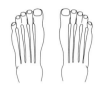

19. Balance Endocrine
    Reflexes

20. Satvic Hold and
    Balance of Big Toes or
    Head/Sacrum Reflex
    Balance

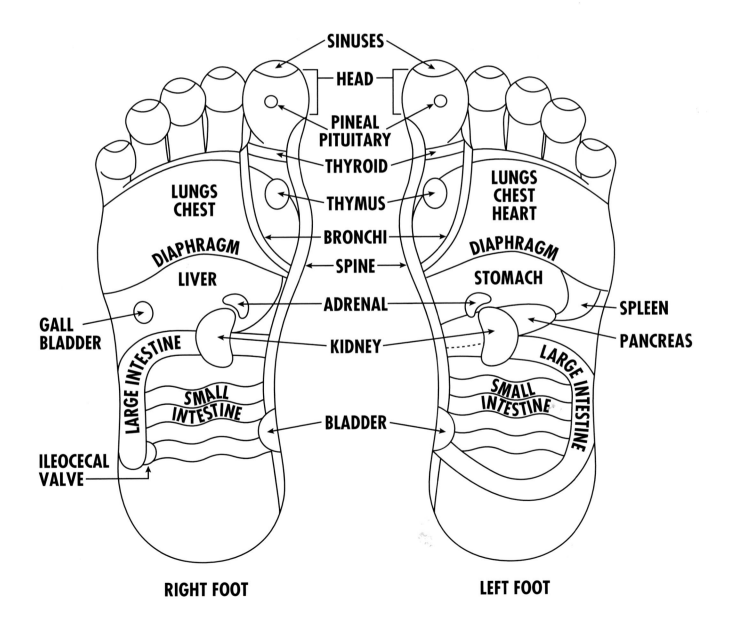

RIGHT FOOT   LEFT FOOT

Foot Cradle: Gently hold the heels of both feet. Apply a very slight inferior traction. Allow yourself to feel the energy up and down the whole body.

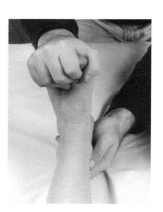 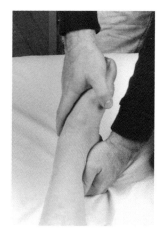

Foot Pump: (Bk II Ch 37) Rest the heel on the palm of one hand and grasp the ball of the foot with your other hand. Lean forward (superiorly) on the foot using your body weight to give the Achilles tendon a good stretch. Then place your hand over the center of the top of the foot and pull downward. The two movements should create a gentle pumping motion. Repeat several times on each foot with a "Watery" rhythm.

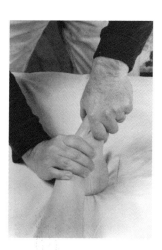 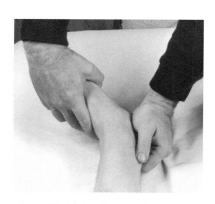

Ankle Rotation and Sidebending: Hold the foot at the top of the ankle and twist it from side to side. Then stabilize the foot at the heel and rotate the foot in all directions.

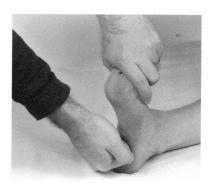

Knuckle Rub: Make a fist with one hand and grasp the toes and top of the foot with your other hand. Pull backward to open up the foot while sliding your knuckles upward.

South Pole Stretch: (Bk II Ch 38, Fig. 4, 5)
Stabilize the leg by holding it above the ankle with one hand; grasp the heel with your other hand and gently pull downward (inferiorly), creating a gentle stretch. This may also be done by grasping the foot with both thumbs on the diaphragm reflex area and your fingers securely interlocking over the the top of the foot. With the foot perpendicular to the table, gently pull downward until you feel resistance. Then have your client inhale and, as they exhale, give a gentle downward thrust.

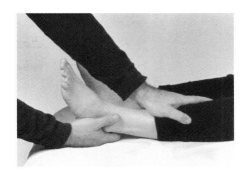

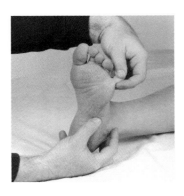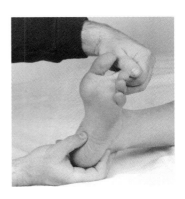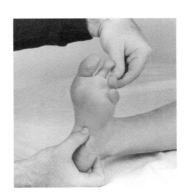

Element Thumb Walk: With the thumb and index finger of one hand, grasp the small toe (Earth element) stretching it upward and back (superiorly). With the thumb of the other hand, "walk up" the element line from the heel to the base of the toe. Repeat with the other toes/elements.

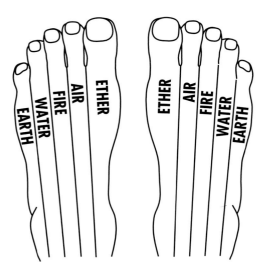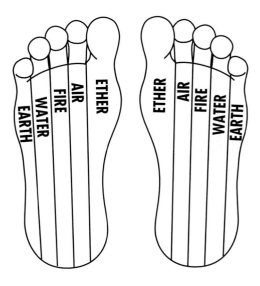

Element Toe Stretch with Superior Tendon Walk: Grasp and stretch the big toe (Ether element) while at the same time walking or sliding your thumb along the corresponding superior tendon on the top of the foot, from the base of the toe toward the ankle. Repeat for the other toes/elements.

 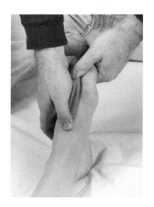 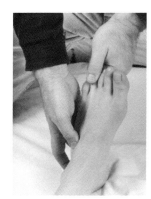 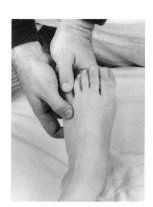

Element Toe Pulls: Firmly grasp the base of the big toe (Ether element) between your thumb and index finger. The index finger should be bent at a right angle. It should feel as though the toe is firmly sandwiched between your fingers. Place your other hand around the first for support as shown. Relax your arms and shoulders and, moving from your center, gently pull the toe downward (inferiorly), allowing your body weight to do the work rather than your forearms. At the end of each pull you may also lift the toe and shake it rhythmically. Be gentle. Repeat for the other toes/elements.

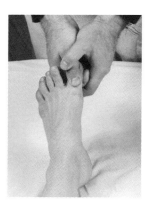 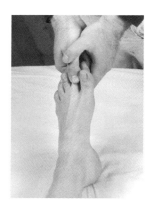 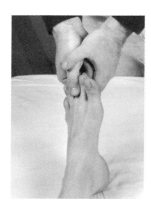 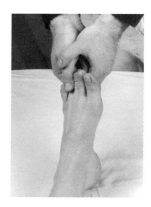

For the following reflexes, first use the thumb walk technique to explore the reflex area. Then, tune into the energy and experiment with applying different types of touch (satvic, rajasic, tamasic, and unwinding) until you find the one that feels "right" for that reflex. Notice any places of tightness/restriction, flaccidity, pain, "crystals," heat, cold or shaking. Stop at areas that call for your attention and "run energy through." You may also make a Polarity energy circuit by holding a point on the foot with one hand and placing your other hand or finger(s) on or over the corresponding part of the body or on the corresponding reflex on the hand, ear or other foot. If these points are too far apart for you to reach comfortably, bend the person's leg at the knee and allow the knee to rest, without effort, against your shoulder.

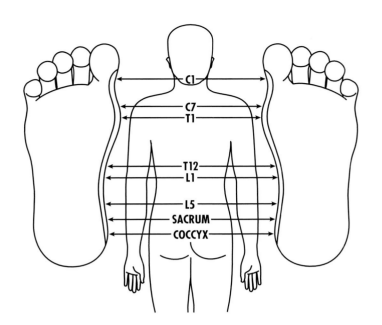

C1
C7
T1
T12
L1
L5
SACRUM
COCCYX

Balance Spinal Reflexes: (Bk II Ch 17, Bk V Ch 19) Rotate the foot to the outside (laterally) to open up the spinal reflex region. Beginning at the atlas (C1) reflex, thumb walk down the neck and spine to the coccyx, identifying the various spinal regions as you go: cervical, thoracic, and lumbar spine, sacrum, coccyx. To make a Polarity energy circuit, note approximately where you are in relationship to the spine (*i.e.,* T7, C4, L5, etc.) and place your other hand or finger(s) on the muscles alongside the corresponding part of the spine. [BW: III.B2]

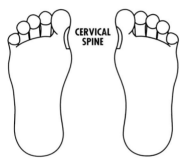

CERVICAL SPINE

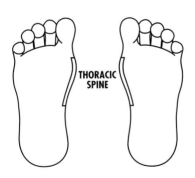

THORACIC SPINE

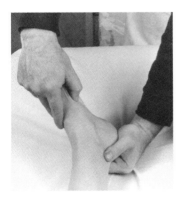

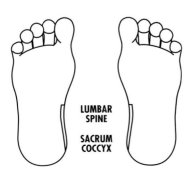

LUMBAR SPINE

SACRUM COCCYX

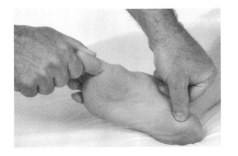

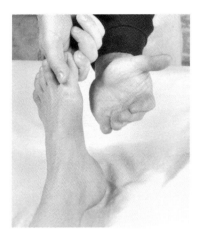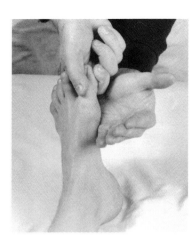

Big Toe Adjustment: (Bk II Ch 37; Bk III Ch 7) Hold the big toe between your thumb and first finger and gently pull. Open your other hand as shown and "chop" with a moderate speed where the arch begins (just below the metatarsophalangeal joint). You should see a subtle ripple effect move up the entire body to the top of the head if the move is done correctly. [BW: II.B9]

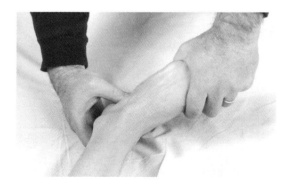

Arch Adjustment through the Cuboid: (Bk II Ch 38, Fig. 1, 2) Side bend the foot toward the midline, place your thumb on the cuboid bone (halfway between the heel and toes), and press upward toward the base of the fifth metatarsal. Deepen pressure by rotating the foot back into your thumb or make a quick short thrust. [BW: V.A1a]

Balance Head and Sinus Reflexes: (Bk II Ch 17, 32; Bk V Ch 4; EES Ch 5, 6) Press, squeeze, and knead the ends and sides of the toes. These points may be very sensitive if a sinus condition or head cold exists.

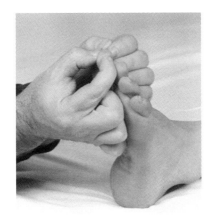
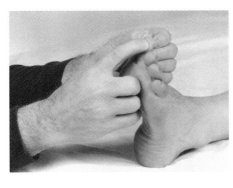

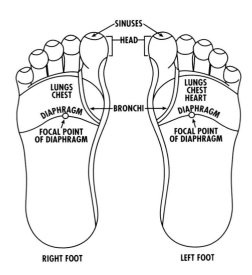

RIGHT FOOT   LEFT FOOT

Balance Heart and Lung Reflexes:
The heart reflex is located on the upper part of the left foot. The lung reflexes are located in the same region on both feet. When chest congestion is present, work deeply in horizontal lines toward the bronchial reflex area between the Ether and Air toes. *See diagram at left.*

Balance Respiratory Diaphragm Reflexes: (Bk II Ch 54, Fig. 5; Bk V Ch 4, 5) This move can be done in several ways. Grasp the heel with one hand and, with the other, press your thumb into the diaphragm reflex. Or, gently place your thumbs over the diaphragm reflexes of both feet and "channel energy." You may also grasp the foot with both hands and, with your thumbs overlapping on the focal point of the diaphragm reflex, press in and upward toward the toes.

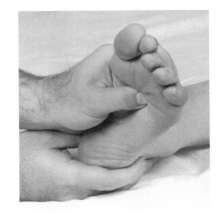
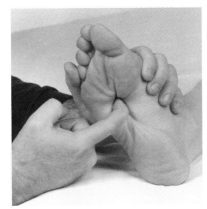

Location of Focal Point of
Diaphragm Reflex

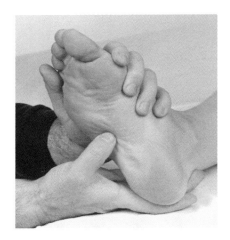

Balance Liver/Gallbladder Reflexes:
The liver and gallbladder reflexes are located on the right foot. Work this area in different directions using the type of touch that feels most appropriate.

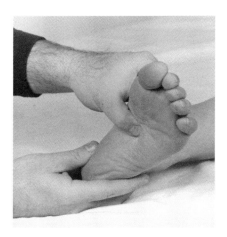

Balance Stomach/Pancreas/ Spleen Reflexes: The stomach, pancreas, and spleen reflexes are located on the left foot. Work this area in different directions using the type of touch that feels most appropriate.

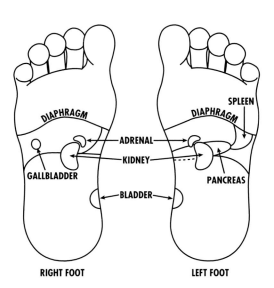

RIGHT FOOT   LEFT FOOT

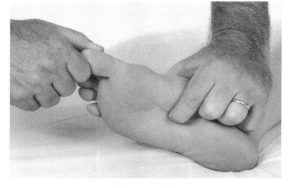

Kidney Reflex

Balance Kidney/Adrenal Reflexes: (Bk II Ch 17, Fig. 3, 4) To find the kidney reflex, grasp the top of the foot and, pulling the foot back, feel for a distinctive area of denser or softer tissue along the Air and Fire lines at the level of the base of the fifth metatarsal bone. The adrenal reflex is located on the Air line, just above the kidney reflex. End your work with each of these reflexes by gently holding the reflexes on both feet at once and channeling energy through them, as if you were recharging a battery.

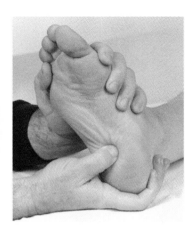
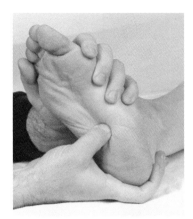
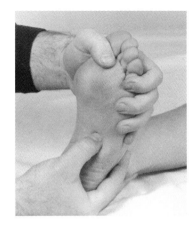

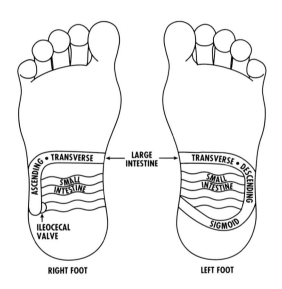

ASCENDING • TRANSVERSE ←→ LARGE INTESTINE ←→ TRANSVERSE • DESCENDING

SMALL INTESTINE

SMALL INTESTINE

SIGMOID

ILEOCECAL VALVE

RIGHT FOOT   LEFT FOOT

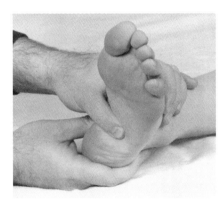

Balance Large Intestine/Small Intestine Reflexes: Work the large intestine reflex from its beginning, at the ileocecal valve on the right foot, to its ending, above the inner heel of the left foot. Pay special attention to the ileocecal valve reflex. Then, work across the area of the small intestine reflexes, within the inner borders of the large intestine reflexes on both feet.

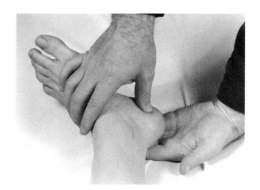

Inside Heel Press: (Bk II Ch 31, 32) Support the heel of the foot with your fingers. With the thumb of your other hand, find a sore spot on the inside of the heel. Press steadily and firmly (tamasically) into the sore spot. Be sensitive to your client's boundaries and always ask them for feedback. *Warning: This area contains the reflex for the uterus. Do not press during pregnancy.* [BW: I.A4]

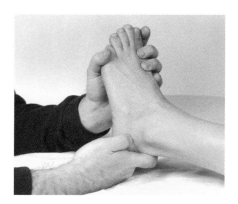

Outside Heel Press: (Bk II Ch 31, 32) Support the foot with the fingers and palm of one hand. With the thumb of your other hand, locate a sore spot on the outside heel. Press steadily and firmly (tamasically) into the sore spot. Be aware of your client's boundaries and ask for feedback. *Warning: This area contains the reflex for the ovaries. Do not press during pregnancy.*

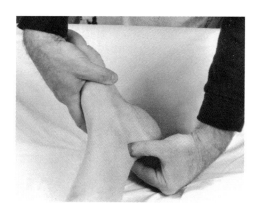

Balance Sciatic Reflexes: (EES Ch 23, Fig. 2) With your thumb and index finger between the achilles tendon and ankle bone, press toward the ankle bone. Press each side separately or both simultaneously.

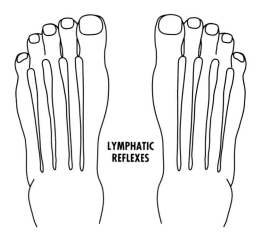

LYMPHATIC REFLEXES

Balance Lymphatic Reflexes: Using the fingertips of both hands, gently stroke the lymphatic reflexes, located between the tendons on the top of the foot. Move from the base of the toes to the ankle, continuing the stroke around and above the ankle to the lower part of the shin and calf. Each stroke should be very slow and continuous with a flowing, "Watery" quality of touch and only very light pressure. Do this several times on each foot.

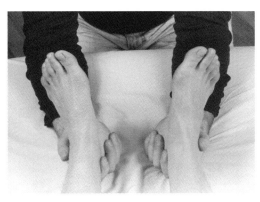

Uterus/Prostate and
Ovaries/Testes Reflexes

Balance Endocrine Reflexes: Hold the uterus/prostate and ovaries/testes reflexes simultaneously on both feet. This may be done by placing your hands around the tops of the ankles or holding the heels, as in the "foot cradle." Hold these points gently and "run energy through." Next, hold the pancreas reflex on the left foot. Continue upward, holding in turn the adrenals, the thymus, and the thyroid/parathyroid reflexes. End by satvically holding the pituitary/pineal reflexes on the big toes.

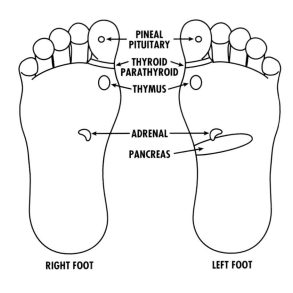

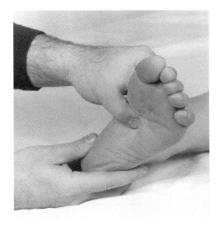

Pancreas Reflex

Satvic Hold and Balance of Big Toes: You may end the session by gently grasping the big toes to balance the energy on both sides of the body, or...

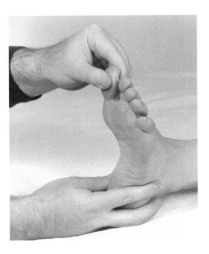

Head/Sacrum Reflex Balance: Gently grasp the big toe and heel and allow the energy to move between your hands.

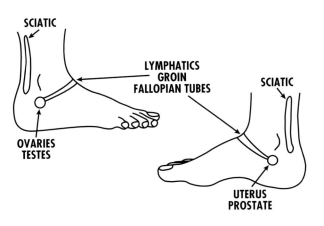

HAND REFLEXOLOGY PROTOCOL

1. Thumb Cradle

2. Element Finger Pulls with Superior Tendon Walk

3. Element Thumb Walk

4. Balance Spinal Reflexes

5. Balance Sinus/Head Reflexes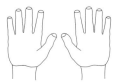

6. Balance Heart/ Lungs/Respiratory Diaphragm Reflexes

7. Balance Digestive System Reflexes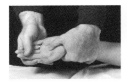

8. Balance Kidney/ Adrenal Reflexes

9. Balance Large Intestine/Small Intestine Reflexes

10. Balance Big Toes and Thumbs

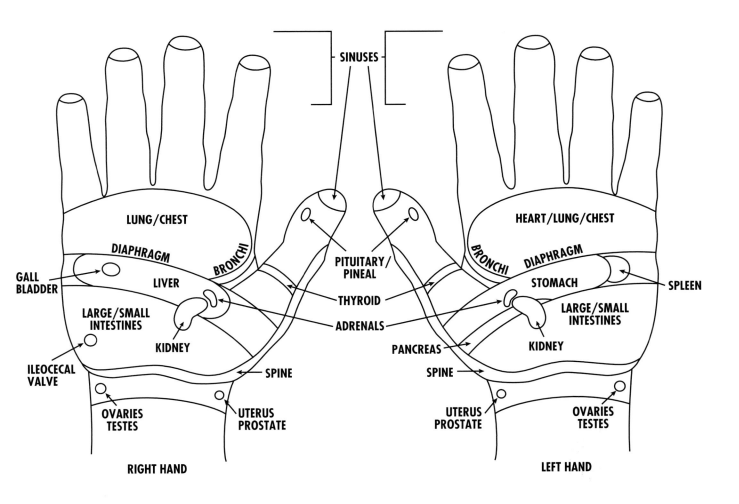

SINUSES

LUNG/CHEST

DIAPHRAGM

BRONCHI

GALL BLADDER

LIVER

LARGE/SMALL INTESTINES

KIDNEY

ILEOCECAL VALVE

OVARIES TESTES

SPINE

UTERUS PROSTATE

RIGHT HAND

PITUITARY/ PINEAL

THYROID

ADRENALS

HEART/LUNG/CHEST

BRONCHI

DIAPHRAGM

STOMACH

SPLEEN

LARGE/SMALL INTESTINES

KIDNEY

PANCREAS

SPINE

UTERUS PROSTATE

OVARIES TESTES

LEFT HAND

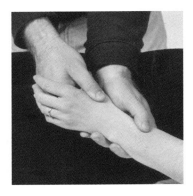

Thumb Cradle: Gently grasp the thumb between your thumb and index finger. Hold without applying any pressure and tune into the energy.

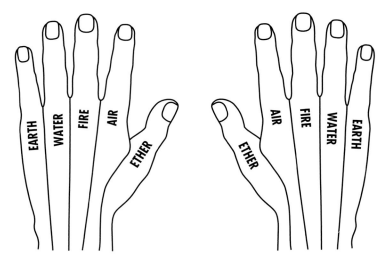

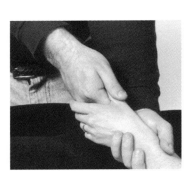

Element Finger Pulls with Superior Tendon Walk: Grasp the base of the thumb (Ether element) between your thumb and index finger. Hold the wrist with your other hand. Gently and firmly pull the thumb away from the wrist, allowing your fingers to slide from the base toward the tip (distally). Repeat for the other fingers/ elements, ending with the little finger (Earth element).

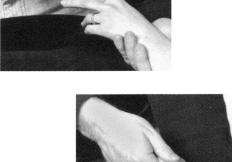

Then, firmly grasp and pull the little finger and, with the thumb of your other hand, walk or slide along the tendon on the back of the hand from knuckle to the wrist. Repeat for the other fingers/elements.

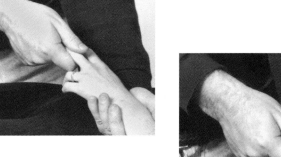

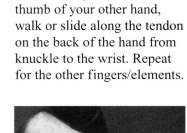

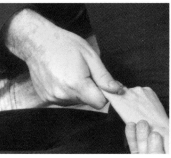

Element Thumb Walk: Open the hand and thumb walk along the Ether, Air, Fire, Water, and Earth energy lines on the palm of the hand between the base of the fingers and the wrist. This may be done in either direction.

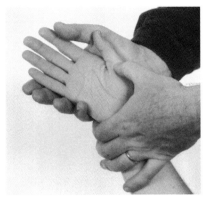

Ether

Air

Fire

Water

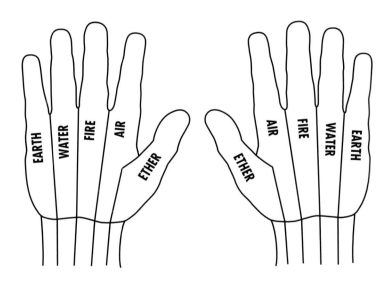

Earth

For the following reflexes, first use the thumb walk technique to explore the reflex area. Then, tune into the energy and experiment with applying different types of touch (satvic, rajasic, tamasic, and unwinding) until you find the one that feels right for that reflex. Notice any places of tightness/constriction, flaccidity, pain, "crystals," heat, cold or shaking. Stop at places that call for your attention and "run energy through." You may also make a Polarity energy circuit by holding a point on the hand with one hand and placing your other hand or finger(s) on or over the corresponding part of the body or on the corresponding reflex of the foot, ear or other hand.

Balance Spinal Reflexes: (Bk V Ch 19; Bk II Ch 17) Open the hand and thumb walk along the neck and spine reflexes, beginning at the atlas (C1) reflex on the side of the thumb. As you work, identify the various spinal regions: cervical, thoracic, and lumbar spine, sacrum, coccyx. To make a Polarity energy circuit, note approximately where you are in a relationship to the spine (*i.e.,* T7, C4, L5, etc.) and place your other hand or finger(s) on the muscles alongside the corresponding part of the spine.

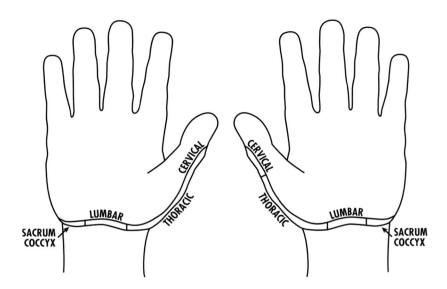

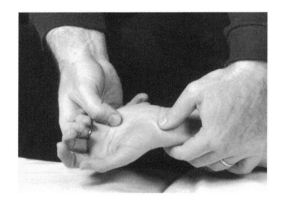

Lumbar Spine

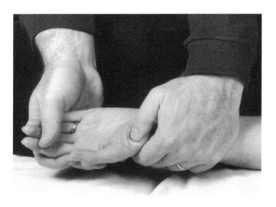

Lower Thoracic Spine

Upper Thoracic Spine

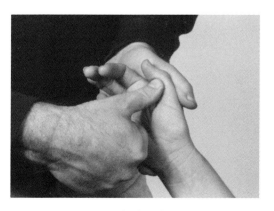

Cervical Spine

Balance Sinus/Head Reflexes: Press, squeeze, and knead the ends and sides of the fingers. These points may be very sensitive if a sinus condition or cold exists. *See diagram below.*

Balance Heart/Lung Reflexes: The heart reflex is located on the upper part of the left palm. The lung reflexes are located in the same region of both palms. When chest congestion is present, work deeply in horizontal lines from the area below the base of the little finger toward the bronchial reflex area in the web between the thumb and index finger.

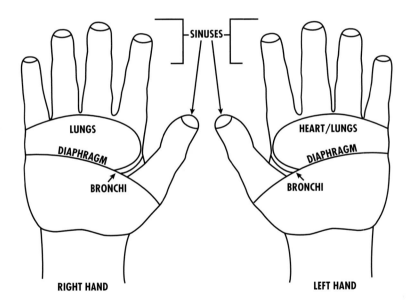

SINUSES

LUNGS

DIAPHRAGM

BRONCHI

RIGHT HAND

HEART/LUNGS

DIAPHRAGM

BRONCHI

LEFT HAND

Balance Respiratory Diaphragm Reflexes: Open the hand and press into the focal point of the respiratory diaphragm reflex with your thumb, as shown. The pressure may vary from gentle to deep.

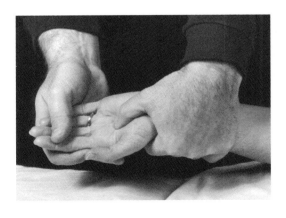

Balance Liver/Gallbladder Reflexes:
The liver and gallbladder reflexes are located in the central region of the right hand. Work this area in different directions using the type of touch that feels most appropriate.

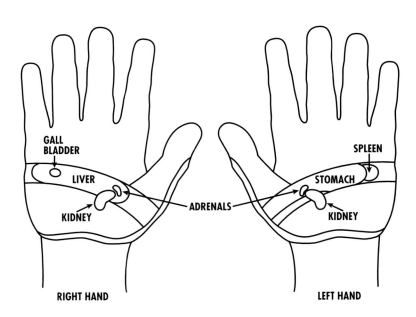

GALL BLADDER

LIVER

KIDNEY

ADRENALS

SPLEEN

STOMACH

KIDNEY

RIGHT HAND

LEFT HAND

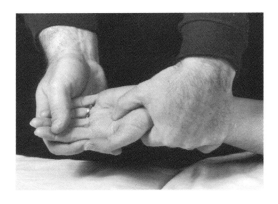

Balance Stomach/Pancreas/Spleen Reflexes:
The stomach, pancreas, and spleen reflexes are located in the central region of the left hand. Work this area in different directions using the type of touch that feels most appropriate.

Balance Kidney/Adrenal Reflexes:
The kidney reflex is located along the Air and Fire lines in the lower portion of the palm. The adrenal reflex is located on the Air line, just next to and slightly above the kidney reflex. End your work with each of these reflexes by gently holding the reflexes on both hands at once and channeling energy through them, as if you were recharging a battery.

Balance Large Intestine/Small Intestine Reflexes:
The large and small intestine reflexes are located
on the lower portion of the palm. Begin by working
these reflexes on the right hand, in a horizontal line
from the ileocecal valve reflex (located below the
little finger) toward the thumb. Then work the
reflexes on the left hand in the opposite direction,
from below the thumb to below the little finger.

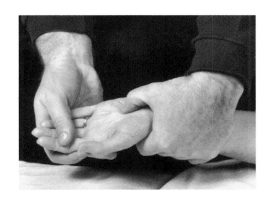

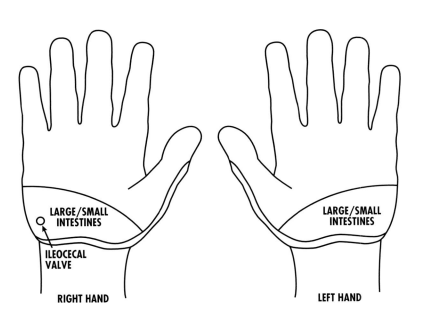

LARGE/SMALL
INTESTINES

ILEOCECAL
VALVE

RIGHT HAND

LARGE/SMALL
INTESTINES

LEFT HAND

Balance Big Toes and Thumbs:
Gently hold the big toe and thumb
until you feel the energy between
them balance. Repeat on the other
side. This can be done on the same
side or diagonally across the body.

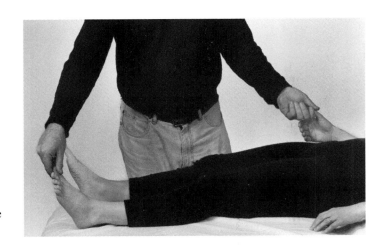

EAR REFLEXOLOGY PROTOCOL

1. Ear Cradle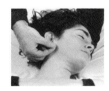

2. South Pole Stretch

3. Stretch and Rotate in Lines of Force

4. Balance Shenmen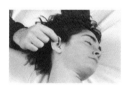

5. Balance Cranial/ Spinal Reflexes

6. Balance Digestive Reflexes

7. Balance Lung/Heart Reflexes

8. Balance Kidney/ Bladder Reflexes

9. Balance Vector Lines Related to Significant Reflexes

10. Little Fingers in Ears Meditation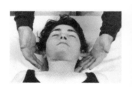

A. Cranium
B. Cervical Spine
C. Thoracic Spine
D. Lumbar Spine
E. Sacrum/Coccyx
F. Lower Jaw Point
G. Heart
H. Lungs
I. Mouth
J. Esophagus
K. Stomach
L. SI
M. LI
N. Spleen
O. Liver
P. Gall Bladder
Q. Pancreas
R. Kidney
S. Ureter
T. Bladder
U. Uterus
V. Point Zero
W. Shenmen
X. Cosmic Receptivity Point
Y. Self-Identity Zone
Z. Wei Qi Command Zone

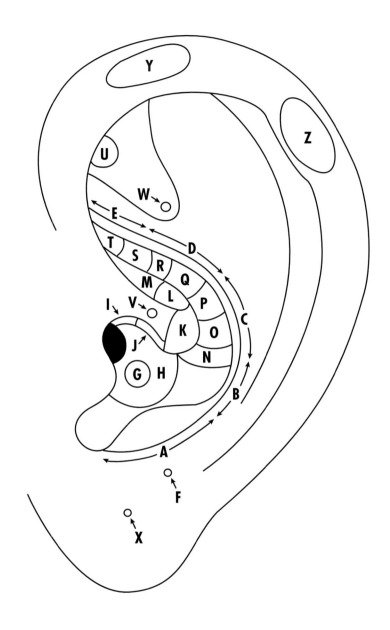

EAR PROTOCOL NOTES

The ears are said to be the passageway to the soul. In the Hindu myth of Vaishvarana, the ears represent "cosmic intelligence" and the four directions of space through which we are able to hear the Holy Words of God. The Chinese saw the ears as spiritual wings. Long ears were signs of wisdom and immortality. The sage Lao-Tzu is oftentimes pictured with seven inch ears and was nicknamed "long ears".

I have presented a reflex mapping of the ear based on the fetal position of a baby in the womb. This is a very effective model developed by Dr. Paul Nogier, a French neurosurgeon and the father of modern auricular therapy. This mapping relates to Dr. Stone's energy tracing and astrological charts which are also based on the fetal position.

Another mapping appears in Dr. Stone's Book II Chart 58, Fig. 3. This mapping shows the body position with the head at the top and the pelvis at the bottom. This mapping is based on the premise of post-natal upright anatomical correspondence.

Both charts are accurate. Remember that the map of a territory can be drawn in many different ways depending upon your perspective. I find the fetal mapping more effective in clinical practice when working with the ear. I also find Dr. Stone's references to and suggestions for working with the ear canal through the tregus exceptional. In fact, the concept of directional lines of force radiating from the ear canal via the tragus is the central organizing pillar of both mappings.

Before you try to understand these mappings through intellectual reasoning, I suggest you do the following exercise. It will help you tune into and experience the source or territory from which the maps are drawn.

EAR TONING EXERCISE

Sit upright, gently place your first fingers in your ears, close your eyes, and hum. Allow your voice to rise and fall in different pitches. Direct the sound to different parts of your cranium. Gently move the tragus in different directions to correspond with the resonance created by the sound at various cranial locations. You can extend the tone up and down your spine and then let it vibrate out to any part of your body.

Ear Cradle: Hold the ear lobe between your thumb and index finger. Hold with a light, secure pressure. Do both ears simultaneously.

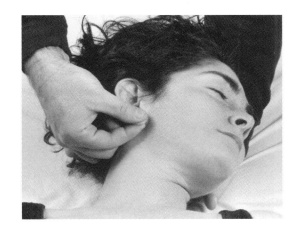

North Pole Stretch: Place one finger in the ear canal and hold the ear lobe between the thumb and index finger of your other hand. Simultaneously stretch the ear lobe and ear canal in opposite directions. Change the angle of your stretch based on palpation feedback. In general, stretch areas of least resistance first and then gradually shift angles to areas of greater resistance.

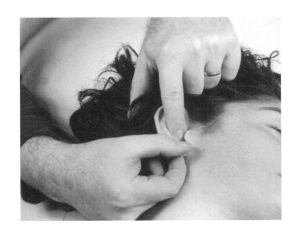

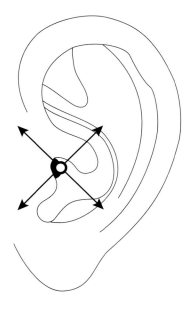

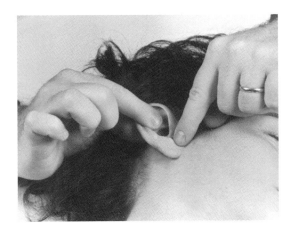

Stretch and Rotate in Lines of Force: Stabilize the tragus with the index finger of one hand as shown and grasp any ear reflex between the thumb and index finger of your other hand. Stretch between the tragus and that reflex and/or create an energy circuit.

Balance Shenmen: Grasp the Shenmen point between your thumb and index finger, as shown. Pressure may vary from gentle to moderate. Do both ears simultaneously.

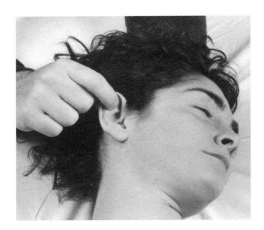

A. Cranium
B. Cervical Spine
C. Thoracic Spine
D. Lumbar Spine
E. Sacrum/Coccyx
W. Shenmen

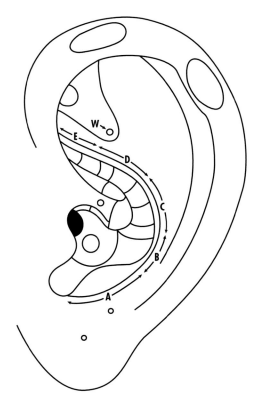

For the following reflexes, hold points between your thumb and index finger, as shown. You may knead the points, apply gentle to moderate pressure or just hold them and "run energy through." You may want to create an energy circuit with corresponding points on the body, the hand or the other ear.

Balance Cranial/Spinal Reflexes: The cranial and spinal reflexes are located along the anti-tragus and the outer rim of the antehelix. Work these reflexes from the head to the sacrum.

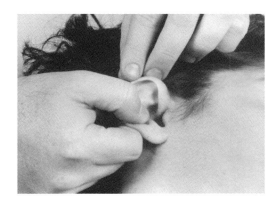

Cranial Reflexes

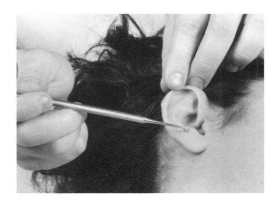

Cervical Reflexes

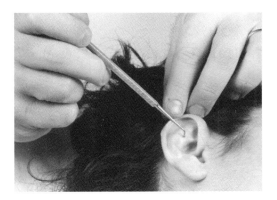

Lumbar Reflexes

Thoracic Reflexes

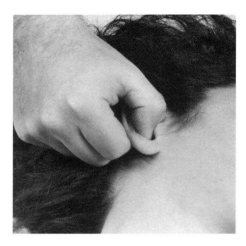

Balance Lung/Heart Reflexes:
The lung and heart reflexes are located in the depression just outside the ear canal (cavum conchae). The heart reflex is in the center of the depression (in both ears) surrounded by the lung reflexes.

G. Heart
H. Lungs
I. Mouth
J. Esophagus
K. Stomach
L. SI
M. LI
N. Spleen
O. Liver
P. Gall Bladder
Q. Pancreas
R. Kidney
S. Ureter
T. Bladder

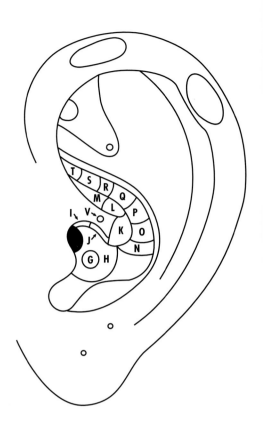

Balance Digestive Reflexes:
The reflexes for the stomach, spleen, pancreas, liver, gallbladder, large intestine, and small intestine are all located in the lower part of the large depression above the crux of the helix (cymba conchae). They can be balanced as a unit or you may balance them separately by focusing your pressure at various angles.

Balance Kidney/Bladder Reflexes:
The kidney and bladder reflexes are located just above the digestive reflexes in the upper part of the depression above the crux of the helix (cymba conchae) and just below the reflexes for the lumbar spine.

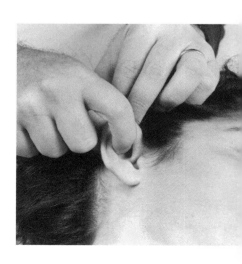

Balance Vector Lines Related to Significant Reflexes: Draw an imaginary line between "point zero" *(see diagram)* and any reflex that draws your attention. Continue the line outward to the rim of the helix. Hold the point on the helix with gentle to moderate pressure. You can make a Polarity energy circuit between this point and point zero or the same point on the other ear or a corresponding point on the body.

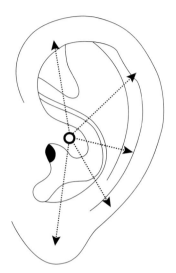 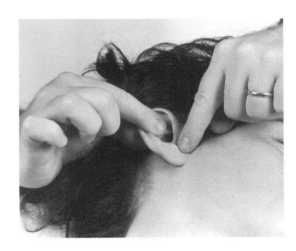

Little Fingers in Ears Meditation: (Bk II Ch 58, Fig 4) Open the palms of your hands and gently place your little fingers just outside the ear canal. Do not press into the canal. Have your client hum until the pitch "feels right" to them, resonating throughout their head and body.

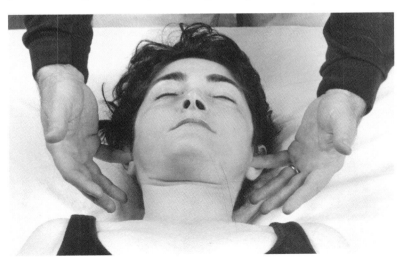

HARMONIC REFLEX PROTOCOL
ENERGY TRACING

Harmonic Reflexes (Bk II Ch 4) are based on the embryonic development and position of the child in the mother's womb. [BW: I.C]

GUIDELINES FOR HARMONIC CHART USE

• Like areas resonate with like areas, i.e. + resonates with +, 0 resonates with 0, and – resonates with –. Always connect two like zones.

• The superior reflex zone is always positive in relationship to the inferior reflex zone.

• An exact point in a reflex zone resonates exactly with all like points in related zones.

• Points may be connected in straight lines or diagonally.

• The left hand contacts the superior positive reflex and the right hand connects the inferior negative reflex.

GUIDES FOR CHOOSING AND TRACING REFLEX POINTS

1. Locate a tender spot.

2. Referring to the chart, note the reflex area in which the tender spot appears. You can use the long line Elemental currents in relationship to the horizontal reflex zones as a grid to determine your location.

3. Locate a corresponding area on your grid above or below the tender spot. This point may also be tender when pressed.

4. Hold both points, creating an energy circuit between your two hands. You may choose to hold the circuit in many ways. You may connect the circuit with your thumbs (Ether), index fingers (Air), etc., or even the palms of your hands. Your touch may vary between tamasic, rajasic, and satvic. Remember to relax and follow the energy. The energy is intelligent and knows exactly what to do.

5. Hold the points until you feel a unity or balance between your hands. You may notice this as a pulse which "ping pongs" between your hands and eventually comes into resonance.

6. When you feel a resonance between your hands, move one of your hands to another corresponding reflex point and make a new connection. You may do this as many times as necessary.

POLARITY HARMONIC ZONES

The following pictures and diagrams are examples of reflex harmonics.

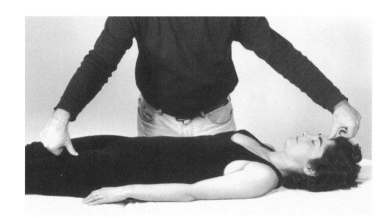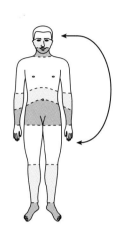

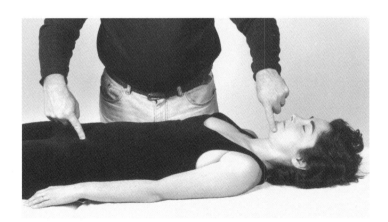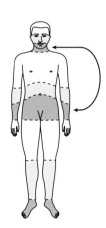

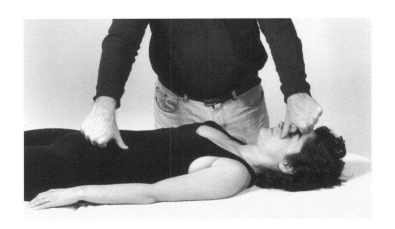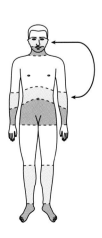

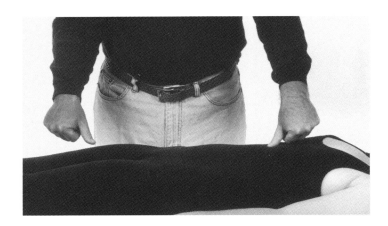
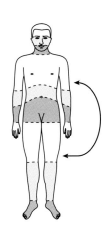

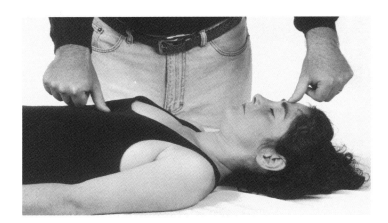
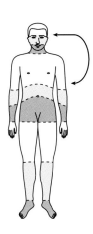

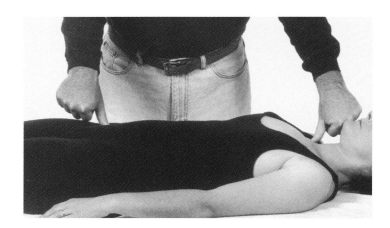
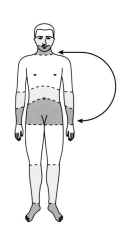

EVALUATION

(Bk III Ch 3; EES Ch 5, 6; Bk V Ch 4; Bk II Ch 58)
[BW: IV.D; EV: 9a]

1. Observe the general shape and proportions of the feet, hands, and ears. What are your visual impressions? For example the feet are big, long, strong, etc. Dr. Stone observed large ear lobes, a large mound of venus in the hands, and large buttocks, as indicators of strong constitutional strength. [EV: 8]

2. Observe any skin coloration and texture changes in relation to the five element currents and reflex areas. This may include scaliness, redness, smoothness, roughness, etc.

3. Observe toe and finger shape and proportion in relation to the five element currents which they represent. For example, the Fire toe is shorter than the Air and Water Toes and is bent at the midline.

4. Observe any foot/hand/ear problems, i.e., corns, bunions, warts, scars, pronation, open sores, infections, etc., and gather the necessary history. Relate those problems to reflex areas and elemental currents.

5. During bodywork continue to identify through palpation any areas of tension (contraction), tenderness, sensitivity, flaccidity (elongation), and excess roughness and note any relationships with reflex areas and the five element currents.

Dr. Stone put an emphasis upon the relationship of the north-south elemental energy currents and their relationship to the toes and fingers. (Bk III Ch 3) Relate your findings to the corresponding elements and the body structures and organs these lines pass through. For example, a curled up little toe relates to the Earth energy line. Emotionally, the earth line represents fear and tissue contraction. Palpating the Earth tendon on the bottom of the foot, you may discover a hard area at the large intestine reflex. Compare the visual relationship of the little toe to your feeling of the reflex. Allow your mind and intuition to simultaneously be with the elemental qualities of Earth, the large intestine, the visual appearance of the little toe, and your overall all sense of the energy. Relax and be aware of what information you receive. Do not try to "figure it out." Just be with the information and wait. If nothing comes, then ask for an answer to come at the appropriate time.

NOTES

Reflex Body Circuits: You may at any time connect a reflex area to a body area by making a circuit. For example, you may be holding the foot reflex point for the lower bowel with one hand and simultaneously place your other hand over the lower bowel area. [BW: IV.D]

Reflex Energy Circuits: You may at any time make a connection along any energy line. For example, you may hold the Water toe with one hand and simultaneously make a circuit with your other hand anywhere along the Water line. [BW: IV.D]

Touching: Three polarity touches are applied to reflex areas:

Satvas: Light touch
Rajas: Rocking touch
Tamas: Deep touch

Traditionally in reflexology a deep touch has been used to "break up crystals." Polarity reflexology uses three touches with the intention of restoring energy flow. One touch is not better than another. All touches work when properly applied.

In relationship to touch, the three principles should be defined in terms of your client's response rather than a preconceived idea. Dr. Stone states: (Bk II pp 65-66)

Satvas: "This must be so fine that it is imperceptible to the tissues and does not arouse them to reaction."

Rajas: "...must have momentum, but no compulsory force which causes a reaction..."

Tamas: "This is the type of therapy where there must be a reaction of soreness, due to greater activity of the re-established life force and circulation in these areas."

Energy Conduction: Polarity Reflexology focuses on life energy. When holding a reflex area, regardless of the touch you choose, remember to tune into the energy. What you feel in your hands can be translated into the five elements and/or your own intuitive language. Listen and respond by "letting your fingers do the walking." The energy will move naturally.

EXERCISE PROTOCOL INTRODUCTION

Polarity Exercise is a series of self-help exercises developed by Dr. Randolph Stone for stimulating and balancing life energy. Polarity exercise focuses on aligning and opening the body through what Dr. Stone referred to as "effortless effort." Rather than doing more, as in externally-directed aerobic and muscle-building exercises, Polarity exercise uses gentle movements to work with the flow of elemental energies.

Polarity exercises should be performed with ease. If any exercise is too difficult for you to do, causing pain or strain, then you should slow down, modify it, or do less. Your ability to do the exercises will change and grow with daily practice. Doing the exercises daily will gradually add strength, tone, and flexibility by increasing your life energy.

Each exercise is based on the Polarity principle of life energy pulsation. It is important to begin and end each exercise in stillness or the Satvic principle. For example, before you do the Woodchopper, stand for twenty seconds in silence. Then begin the active phase of the exercise. This phase stimulates the Rajasic, or outgoing, and Tamasic, or incoming, pulse of life energy. Afterwards, be still for at least 30 seconds. Tune into your physical sensations and allow your body to vibrate with them. Then move on to the next exercise and repeat the process.

Once you have learned the protocols, you may want to improvise based on your individual elemental needs. You may determine the best exercise(s) for you to do by asking the question, "What energy do I need to tune into today?" You may choose some Fire and Air exercises because you want to get going, or you may need to slow down, get in touch with your feelings or ground yourself, so you might choose some Water and Earth exercises. If you feel tight, rigid or tense, you might choose some Ether stretches.

When you understand the energy principles of Polarity, you can create and/or integrate new exercises into your protocol. To make the protocols flowing and fun, we have added several exercises. These exercises are in alignment with Polarity energy principles as well as being included in the latest advances in sports medicine, movement therapy, and injury prevention. These additional exercises include the Neck Rolls, Cross Crawl, Positive Points, Cat Back, Spinal Twist, Psoas Stretch, Sunrise, Wave, and the Prayer Stretch.

Always do your exercises with an easy, joyful attitude. Remember to use "effortless effort." Be patient and allow yourself all the time you need to become more flexible and strong and enjoy your new feelings of vitality and well-being.

POLARITY EXERCISE PROTOCOL #1

(HB: pp. 128-183)

1. Cross
Crawl

6. Up/Down
Ha Breath

11. Wood
Chopper

2. Element
Toe
Stretches

7. Side-to-Side
Ha Breath

12. Pierre
Ha
Breath

3. Leg
Swings

8. Polarity
Squat

13. East-West
Balance

4. Neck Rolls
& Shrugs

9. Sagittarius
Thigh
Sweep

14. Standing
Meditation
Positive
Points

5. Pyramid
Stretch

10. Capricorn
Knee
Circles

Opposite Side Lift   Same Side Lift

Cross Crawl

Opposite Side Lifts: Simultaneously lift your left knee and right arm and, making a big, round movement with your arm, touch your right hand to your left knee. Then do the reverse, lifting your right knee and left arm and touching your left hand to your right knee. Do this 20 times in quick, repetitive motions while your eyes look up and to the left.

Same Side Lifts: Simultaneously lift your left arm and left knee. Then do the reverse, lifting your right arm and right knee. Do this 20 times in quick, repetitive motions while your eyes look down and to the right.

Repeat Opposite Side Lifts.

Benefits: Focuses, centers, and integrates right and left hemispheres of the brain.

Toe Element Stretches (E20)

All Elements—Negative pole

Stand with your feet about 12 inches apart. Begin by shifting your center of gravity over your right leg and bending your right knee for flexible, yet firm, support. Bend your left foot at the toes so that your toes are curled under and their upper (dorsal) surface is pressed against the floor (plantarflexion). Shift your center of gravity back toward the left, pressing your left foot into the floor and stretching the upper tendons. At first, focus the pressure on your big toe (Ether element) while holding the fingers of both hands in the "Ether circuit" described below and visualize the qualities of this element. After a minute or so, focus the pressure on your second toe (Air), then your third (Fire), your fourth (Water), and finally your little toe (Earth). Each time, press and stretch for at least 30 seconds to a minute, holding your fingers in the corresponding energy circuit and visualizing the qualities of the corresponding element. As you do this, allow your body to move with the energy—move your arms, make sounds, etc. Notice which toes are most sensitive. When you are done, shake out your foot and then briefly bend your toes into the floor the other way (dorsiflexion) while holding your fingers in the Ether circuit. Shake out your foot again, then your lower leg, and then your whole leg from the hip (see next exercise). Close your eyes and stand with both feet flat on the floor. Can you feel the energy moving up the energy meridians? Can you feel a difference in the two sides of your body? Repeat on the other foot.

Benefits: Activates all the Elements and circulates their energies throughout the body.

Visualizations for the Elements

Big toe—Ether—blue, space, expression, opening the joints, throat.

2nd toe—Air—green, heart, love, compassion, healing, moving fast, moving out in all directions.

3rd toe—Fire—yellow, action, enthusiasm, determination, solar plexus, digestion, eyes, seeing clearly.

4th toe—Water—orange, feelings, connected, flowing, sensuality, creativity, pelvis.

5th toe—Earth—red, lower back, neck, knees, security, stability, organized, structure, feeling safe.

Finger Circuits

Ether—thumb and index finger or all fingertips together

Air—thumb and index finger

Fire—thumb and middle finger

Water—thumb and ring finger

Earth—thumb and little finger

Leg Swings

These should be done after the Toe Element Stretches. With energy and enthusiasm, swing your whole leg back and forth as far as it will go. Repeat five to ten times for each leg. Do not strain—relax your joints, be playful. It's okay to lose your balance. (You can hold onto something if you like.)

Benefits: Releases the hip joints. Allows the energy of the Elements to flow through the legs and circulate throughout the body.

Neck Rolls

Earth - Positive Pole

Slowly roll your neck in one full circle, breathing into any tight spots. Open your jaw when your head rolls backward. As you roll your neck, make groans and sounds. Do this one time in each direction.

Benefits: Relieves tension and tightness in the neck, shoulders, and jaw.

Neck Shrugs

Breathing deeply, shrug both shoulders while turning your head in a slow full circle. Do one time in each direction.

Pyramid Stretch (HB: pp. 82-83)

All Elements

Stand in the pyramid posture as shown(position 1). Make sure your spine is straight and your neck and shoulders are relaxed, open, and rounded forward. Your elbows should be slightly bent. Take a deep abdominal breath. As you exhale, bring your left shoulder down, forward, and toward the midline while, at the same time, turning your head so that you are looking upward over your right shoulder (position 2). Take another deep breath and, as you exhale, turn your head to the left, so that you are looking down over your left shoulder at your left foot (position 3). Take another deep breath and, as you exhale, return your body to the pyramid posture (position 4). Repeat for the other side (positions 5 & 6). This exercise can also be done while sitting in a chair.

Benefits: Balances five-pointed star, lining up the body with archetypal patterns so energy can flow more freely. The body takes on all of the geometric shapes and triangles of the five-pointed star. Stretches the spine. Releases the hips, pelvis, and shoulders. Lengthens the spine. Opens the diaphragm. Stimulates the production and flow of cerebrospinal fluid. Good for pregnant women.

[SP: A.5a]

Position 1

Position 2

Position 3

Position 4

Position 5

Position 6

Position 1

Up/Down Ha Breath (EES Ch 13)

Ether, Air & Fire Elements

Stand in the pyramid posture (position 1). Take a deep abdominal breath. As you inhale, straighten your arms and lift your torso. Your spine and neck should remain rounded forward (position 2). As you exhale, bring your torso down, parallel to the floor, and make a deep, resonant "HA" sound. Make sure that, as your torso falls, your spine and neck are straight and elongated (position 3). Repeat five times.

Benefits: Releases stuck feelings, frustrations, and pent-up emotions. Releases neck and shoulder tension. Opens the throat and voice. Frees expression of Fire, Air, and Ether Elements.

[SP: A.4a]

Position 2

Position 3

Side-to-Side Ha Breath (EES Ch 14)

Ether, Air & Fire Elements
East-West Energy Currents

This is a variation of the Pyramid Stretch using sound; the movements are exactly the same as steps 1 and 2: Stand in the pyramid posture (position 1). Take a deep abdominal breath and, as you exhale, make a deep, resonant "HA" sound, while bringing your left shoulder forward and turning your head to look up over your right shoulder (position 2). Take another deep breath and, as you exhale, return your body to the pyramid posture (position 3). Repeat for the opposite side (position 4).

Benefits: Balances the Air element. Stimulates the flow of East/West energy currents. Frees expression. Brings your energy outward.

[SP: A.4c]

Position 1

Position 2

Position 3

Position 4

Squat (HB: pp. 130-151; 176-178)

All elements

Bend your knees and come down into a squat position as shown below. Relax your neck, spine, and shoulders. Your feet should be flat on the floor. If your heels do not reach the floor, place a rolled-up towel, pillow, or book under them for support. Rock back and forth and side to side while holding this posture. Feel free to make sounds.

Note: If the regular squat position is difficult, you can do a modified squat by bending down halfway or holding onto the knobs on either side of an open door, bending your knees, relaxing your neck, and rocking the pelvis back and forth.

Benefits: Releases gas. Relieves indigestion and constipation. Tones abdominal muscles and organs. Opens spine and joints. Aligns chakras and allows energy to flow more freely throughout the body. Opens space around the kidneys. Stretches and relaxes muscles of the pelvic floor and perineum. Relieves a heavy, waterlogged feeling. Improves posture and ability to walk freely and lightly. Relieves back pressure, menstrual cramps, and PMS. Grounds, centers, and calms the mind. Rejuvenates and recharges.

Variations:

Wise Man of Old

Interlace your fingers and place your thumbs on the inside of your eye sockets as shown. Let your head fall onto your thumbs and rock.

[SP: A.3h]

Youth Posture (Bk II Ch 64)

Place your elbows between your knees and push your knees outward as shown. Interlock your fingers and breathe deeply.

[SP: A.2a]

Spinal Stretch

Interlace your fingers, place them on the back of your head, and pull your head down toward your chest, stretching your spine. Angle the pull toward the right, then the left, then the center.

[SP: A.3c]

Position 1

Position 2

Sagittarius Thigh Rub

Fire Element

Bend your knees slightly and bend forward with your palms on the tops of your thighs as shown (position 1). Drop your head so that your neck is straight, breathe in and, as you breathe out, sweep your palms downward toward your knees, lifting them off at the end of the sweep. As you sweep down, make a loud, fiery "RAM" sound (position 2). Repeat five times.

Benefits: Brings out Sagittarius Fire. Motivates. Propels forward into action. Stimulates the Fire of Life and brings our ideas out to light the Fire of Life in the world.

Capricorn Knee Circles

Earth & Fire Elements

Stand with your legs together, knees bent, and your hands just above your knees as shown. Make circles with your knees 10 times to the right and then 10 times to the left.

Benefits: Brings energy down the legs to stimulate Sagittarius Fire and Capricorn Earth. Grounds and sustains Fire. Brings out the balance and tenacity of the Capricorn goat who can stand and balance in the most rugged mountain terrains.

Caution: If you have knee problems, be careful not to put too much pressure on your knee joints.

Position 1   Position 1

Wood Chopper (EES Ch 13)

Ether, Air & Fire Elements

As you breathe in, lift your arms over your head as if you were holding an axe. Your pelvis should be tipped forward and the small of your back arched as shown (position 1). As you breathe out, make a loud "HA" sound while bringing your arms forward, curving your chest downward, and tilting your pelvis back, as if you were chopping wood (position 2).

Benefits: Releases stuck feelings, frustrations, and pent-up emotions. Frees expression of Fire, Air and Ether Elements. Releases tension along spine, pelvis, neck, and shoulders.

Position 2   Position 2

Pierre Ha Breath

Fire, Air & Ether Elements

Stand with your feet together and your arms out in front of you. Focus your eyes on a spot several feet beyond your fingertips. Take three short, quick in-breaths through your nose, each time crossing your hands one over the other (positions 1, 2 & 3). Then, simultaneously, open your arms wide, lift up on your toes, and make a loud "HA" sound. Make sure your neck lengthens and your jaw relaxes as you make the sound. You should feel like a bird taking off, about to fly (position 4).

Benefits: Draws energy upward in the body. Opens the throat and voice. Releases stuck feelings, frustrations, and pent-up emotions. Frees expression of Fire, Air, and Ether Elements.

Position 1

Position 2

Position 3

Position 4

East-West Balance

East-West Energy Currents

Stand with your feet together, your arms bent at the elbows, and your index fingers and thumbs touching as shown. Breathe in through your nose as you turn your upper body to the left (position 1). Then breathe out through your mouth as you turn your upper body to the right (position 2). Repeat these movements rapidly at first and then gradually slow down until you come to rest at the center. Feel the energy swirling around you.

Benefits: Energizes and balances East-West energy currents. Stimulates the production and distribution of cerebrospinal fluid.

Position 1

Position 2

Standing Meditation

Positive Points

Ether Element

Stand with your feet together and knees slightly bent. Close your eyes and breathe deeply. Cross your thumbs over your chest as shown and touch your sternum. Visualize a positive experience.

Benefits: Anchors a Higher Self experience in the body and sends a flood of positive sensations throughout the cells for future reference and present recall.

Brain Buttons

Ether Element

Stand with your feet together and knees slightly bent. Place your left hand over your navel and your right hand on your chest as shown. Close your eyes and breathe deeply. Repeat with hands reversed.

Benefits: Integrates right and left brain hemispheres.

POLARITY EXERCISE PROTOCOL #2

(HB: pp. 128-183)

1. Sunrise

7. The Rower

13. Cat Back

2. The Wave

8. Rock & Roll

14. Prayer Stretch

3. Cliffhanger

9. Psoas Stretch

15. Motor Balance

4. Wise Man of Old

10. Spinal Twist

16. Sensory Balance

5. Ha Frog

11. Partner Diaphragm Release

6. Windshield Wipers

12. The Scissors

Position 1   Position 2   Position 3

Sunrise

Ether Element
Ultrasonic Core

Stand with your heels together, knees bent, and your hands in the prayer position as shown (position 1). Take a deep breath in while straightening your knees and bringing your arms up over your head; let your head and eyes follow your hands (position 2). As you exhale, bend your knees and allow your arms to fall open to your sides with palms facing outward; let your head fall back with your jaw relaxed and mouth open (position 3). Stay in this position for a few seconds feeling a sense of openness and freedom. Then, as you breathe in, bring your arms back up over your head (position 4). As you breathe out, bring your arms down and your hands back to the prayer position (position 5).

As you do this exercise, visualize that you are a flower opening in the first light of the morning or that you are surrounded by the most beautiful, vibrant color you can imagine or that you are a sunrise opening up to the light and then returning to your center (the Ultrasonic Core).

Benefits: Awakens, focuses, and centers the mind and body. Brings the energy of all the Elements into the center of the body. Opens and energizes the Ultrasonic Core. Helps us find the place inside to begin and end from. Opens the space of Ether and expression. Releases tension in the neck and between the shoulder blades.

Position 4   Position 5

Position 1

Position 2

Position 3

The Wave

Water Element

This exercise should be done in one long, flowing, continuous motion.

Begin by standing with your knees bent and your right foot slightly behind the left. As you breathe in, move your center of gravity back over your right foot and raise your forearms as shown (position 1). As you breathe out, bring your body forward, palms first (position 2), until your center of gravity is over left foot, your arms are outstretched, and the back of your right foot comes up off the floor (position 3). Then return to the first position. As you move, make sure your neck and shoulders are relaxed. Use your whole body. Imagine your whole body becoming a wave.

Benefits: Increases circulation. Lets energy move freely. Brings out the qualities of the Water Element. Helps to develop connected and creative patterns of movement.

Cliff Hanger
(HB: pp. 179-181)

Ether & Air Elements

Beginners' Cliff Hanger: Stand with your lower spine against a table, counter or tall chair. Make sure the surface is sturdy and stable enough to support your weight without tipping over. Place your palms on the edge of the surface and your feet flat on the floor about 12 inches apart. Bend your knees and let your torso drop straight down toward the floor while your head falls forward onto your chest, as shown. Remain in this position for 30 seconds to several minutes, relaxing your abdomen and pelvis. Take deep abdominal breaths and, as you exhale, make deep "AAH" sounds. Slowly bring your body back up to a standing position. Close your eyes and take a moment to feel the still point, a moment of space in which all things have a chance to reorganize.

Advanced Cliffhanger: The movement is the same as described above; the variation is in the breathing. As you begin, take a deep breath in through your nose, drop your torso down toward the floor, and exhale **completely.** Take a step forward and come into a standing position. Stand for a moment, "empty," feeling the still point, and then take a deep breath in.

Benefits: Releases shoulder tension. Moves energy blocks in shoulders and hips. Deep breathing creates a vacuum in the chest followed by a flood of energy throughout the body which deeply rejuvenates all of the organs.

[SP: A.5b]

Wise Man of Old

Bend your knees and come down into a squat position as shown. Relax your neck, spine, and shoulders. Your feet should be flat on the floor. If your heels do not reach the floor, place a folded towel, pillow or book under them for support. Interlace your fingers and place your thumbs on the inside of your eye sockets. Let your head fall forward onto your thumbs. Rock back and forth and side to side.

Benefits: See page 120.

Ha Frog
(EES Ch 15)

Ether & Fire Elements

Bend over with your knees slightly bent and grasp the inner arches of your feet as shown (position 1). Take a deep breath in and, as you exhale, bend your knees and bring your body down into a squat position while making a loud "HA" sound (position 2). Repeat 5 times.

Benefits: Releases tension in the diaphragm. Releases stuck feelings, frustration, and pent-up emotions. Opens the voice and throat.

Position 1

Position 2

Position 1

Position 2

Windshield Wipers

Sit on the floor as shown and roll your legs back and forth from the hip joint. Do this for at least five minutes with an even, flowing movement.

Benefits: Increases circulation in the ankles, calves, thighs, and hips. Relaxes the lower back and piriformis muscles. Relieves leg cramps, sciatic pain, and swelling of the ankles. Improves mobility of the hip joint.

Position 3

Position 1

Position 2

The Rower

Water Element

Sit on the floor with your knees bent and your feet and toes flexed back toward your shins as shown (position 1). If you are unable to reach your toes, grasp your ankles, shins or lower thighs above your knees. Begin "rowing" by moving the balls of your feet toward the floor and rounding your neck, shoulders, and upper back toward your toes (position 2), and then returning to the first position (position 3). Row forward and back for several minutes, making sure your neck and chin remain rounded forward and relaxed. This exercise can also be done with a partner as shown below.

Benefits: Stretches the upper and lower back, hamstrings, calves, and ankles. Increases circulation. Relieves swelling of the ankles and cold feet. Stimulates the nervous system along the spine.

Position 3

Position 1

Rock & Roll

Water Element

Begin by sitting on the floor with knees bent and hands grasping the thighs as shown (position 1). Your hands may grasp anywhere along the inner or outer thighs.* You may cross your arms between your legs to hold points on your thighs if this is more comfortable. Keeping your back and neck rounded forward, roll backward toward the floor drawing your knees toward your chest (positions 2 & 3) and then return to a sitting position by pulling your thighs away from your chest. Repeat 20 times in a continuous, flowing movement.

Benefits: Releases neck, throat, and shoulder tension. Strengthens iliopsoas, gluteus maximus, back, and abdominal muscles. Strengthens heart. Stimulates circulation of cerebrospinal fluid.

*Points along the outer thigh reflex inversely to the back of the neck—i.e., points just above the knees reflex to the upper neck near the cranium and points near the hips reflex to the lower neck and shoulders. Points on the inner thighs reflex inversely to the front of the neck and throat.

Position 2

Position 3

Position 1

Position 2

Position 3

Psoas Stretch

Sit on the floor with your knees bent as shown; relax your lower back, let your weight sink down into the floor, and reach down to the right with your right hand as if you were scooping up sand (position 1). Then, scoop the sand up to the sky, lifting your right arm and hip upward as far as they can go (position 2). Imagine that someone is holding your right hand exactly where it is and then let your buttocks drop down to the floor. Next, round back and curve your pelvis forward as you curl your right arm down to the left, bringing your hand through the "tunnel" between your left hip and arm (position 3). In this position, relax your neck and shoulders as you take three deep breaths. Repeat on the other side.

Benefits: Stretches psoas muscles. Releases tension along the spine and between the shoulder blades. Relieves back pain caused by shortened psoas muscles.

Spinal Twist

Lying on your back, bring your left knee up to your chest, grasping it with your right hand. Twist your lower body to the right, using your right hand to draw your left knee toward the floor on your right and raise your left arm diagonally up to the left as shown. Look up at your left hand. Try to keep your right shoulder on the floor, bringing the knee up a little if you need to, so you don't strain your shoulder. Take at least three deep breaths, relaxing the muscles in your spine, shoulders, jaw, and neck. Feel free to make groans or any sounds. Repeat on the other side.

Benefits: Opens up and releases tension in the spine, hips, shoulders, chest, and diaphragm.

Position 1

Position 2

Partner Diaphragm Release
(Bk IV Ch 11)

Have your partner lie down on the floor with the left knee bent; stand with your feet on either side of their hips and place both of your hands gently on the area of the diaphragm, just below the ribs (position 1). Find the center point just below the sternum where the xyphoid process is located. DO NOT PRESS DIRECTLY ON THIS POINT. With your thumbs, contact points along the lower edge of the ribcage about two inches to the side of this central point. Ask your partner to breathe in and then exhale slowly as they lift their right leg off the floor as shown (position 2). At the height of the lift, ask them to inhale again and, as they exhale, slowly lower their right leg to the floor (position 3). Ask your partner to breathe normally for a moment or so and then repeat the process while raising the other leg. (You may use the same or different contact points along the edge of the ribs.) During this exercise, the contact along the ribcage may be gentle to deep, but be very sensitive about the amount of pressure you use—make sure your partner lets you know if the pressure becomes too strong. Also, both you and your partner should feel free to make sounds during the exhale.

Position 3

Benefits: Promotes full, deep breathing. Releases tension in the diaphragm. Tension in the diaphragm has wide-ranging effects, both physically and energetically. Dr. Stone tells us that the diaphragm is the "tree of life, with its roots in the chest and branches in the head." It divides the upper body from the lower body and the Air and Fire Elements from the Water and Earth Elements. It supports the functioning of the lungs, heart, and abdominal organs and is the entrance to the solar plexus—the source of our power, enthusiasm, and ability to take action.

[SP: A.6b]

Position 1

Position 2

Position 3

The Scissors
(Bk II Ch 52)

Lie face down with your forehead on your hands and knees bent and about shoulder-width apart as shown (position 1). Breathe deeply while crossing and uncrossing your ankles rapidly for several minutes (positions 2 & 3).

Benefits: Opens sinuses. Relieves tension in the piriformis and other hip muscles.

Position 1

Position 2

Cat Back

Kneel on the floor as shown, with your hands on the floor directly under your shoulders and your knees directly under your hips; arch your back, letting your stomach and ribs drop down toward the floor while stretching your chin up toward the ceiling (position 1). Take three deep breaths. Then reverse the stretch, curling your spine upward like a cat, bringing your chin in toward your chest, and exhaling completely as you pull your stomach in and up toward your spine (position 2). Inhale and exhale deeply three times and then return to the first position. Repeat several times.

Benefits: Stretches spine. Increases flexibility, circulation, and ease of movement. Relieves back stiffness.

Prayer Stretch

Kneel on the floor with your arms stretched out in front of you as shown. Rest your forehead on the floor and let your head and neck relax. Keep your spine as straight as possible as your reach forward with your fingers and backward with your hips. Breathe deeply and relax into the stretch. To move out of this position, curl your toes up under your ankles and rock back onto your feet as you lift your hips and buttocks up toward the ceiling. Relax for a moment with your head and arms dangling toward the floor, then slowly roll up to a standing position, vertebra by vertebra, letting your head come up last. Stand for a moment and breathe deeply.

Benefits: Lengthens and stretches spine, improving circulation and freeing spinal nerves. Releases areas of tension along the back. Increases flexibility and ease of movement.

Motor Balance
(Bk V Ch 90)

Sit on the floor with your arms gently wrapped around your knees as shown. Let your head drop forward so your chin is resting on your chest. Round your back, close your eyes, and breathe deeply. This can also be done with your hands wrapped around the base of your skull and elbows resting on your knees.

Benefits: Relaxes, lengthens, and stretches the neck and back. This is an active, energizing (Yang) position, good to do after vigorous exercise.

[SP: A.7a]

Sensory Balance
(Bk V Ch 9)

Sit cross-legged on the floor with your spine straight and arms crossed as shown. Rest your hands gently on your ankles. Relax your shoulders, neck, and jaw. Close your eyes and breathe deeply.

Benefits: Calms, centers, and rejuvenates. This is a receptive, open (Yin) position, good to do when you are stressed out or overloaded (*e.g.,* when you are listening to a lecture and have lost your concentration).

[SP: A.7b]

STRUCTURAL ALIGNMENT PROTOCOLS INTRODUCTION

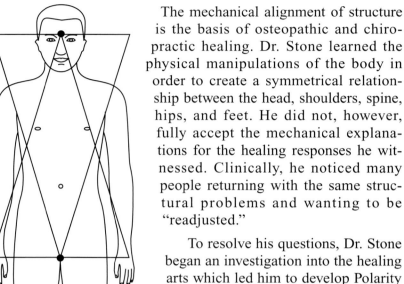

The cranial, spinal, and facial balancing protocols are designed to help you learn the art of Polarity structural alignment. The guiding pattern for structural alignment in Polarity is the six-pointed star. Anatomically, the six-pointed star begins its downward triangle at the sphenoid/occiput articulation and its upward triangle at the junction of the sacrum and coccyx.

Energetically, the downward pointing triangle of the six-pointed star represents the masculine energy of the Father, or Sun. This energy steps downward in vibration and creates the oval fields, or "structural spaces." Oval fields are like houses or open fields. Physically, the oval fields are formed by the transfascial planes.

The upward pointing triangle of the six-pointed star represents the feminine energy of the Mother or Moon. It steps upward in vibration and creates the five chakras as centers of expressive energy. The energy of the chakras fills the empty spaces of the oval fields with creative/elemental movement.

A harmonious, symmetrical relationship between the two triangles is necessary for healing. Proper structural alignment, the principle represented by the six-pointed star pattern, supports the expression of each element. For example, if a dancer wants to dance, she must have a solid and secure dance floor on which to move. A pianist must have a structurally correct and properly tuned piano in order to press the keys and express himself.

The mechanical alignment of structure is the basis of osteopathic and chiropractic healing. Dr. Stone learned the physical manipulations of the body in order to create a symmetrical relationship between the head, shoulders, spine, hips, and feet. He did not, however, fully accept the mechanical explanations for the healing responses he witnessed. Clinically, he noticed many people returning with the same structural problems and wanting to be "readjusted."

To resolve his questions, Dr. Stone began an investigation into the healing arts which led him to develop Polarity Therapy. Polarity takes into account the holistic relationship between structural alignment, thought processes, emotional expression, and spiritual awareness. In Polarity, healing is much more than just the mechanical adjustment of the spine and extremities.

So, although many of the structural moves presented in these chapters may resemble chiropractic and osteopathic manipulations, remember that they have been re-thought and modified in the context of the Polarity Therapy paradigm. Dr. Stone refers to them as "old moves with a new emphasis."

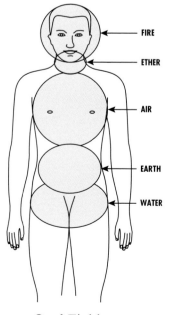

Oval Fields

Due to the complexity of many of these moves, it is recommended that you learn how to do the protocols in this section from a qualified teacher with thorough anatomy training and palpation experience.

CRANIAL BALANCING
INTRODUCTION

Dr. Stone did not leave us many charts on the practice of cranial balancing; however, he did emphasize its value and place in Polarity Therapy. He states, "The life-breath of the prana current moves in the cerebrospinal fluid conductor to all tissues and cells, communicating with other internal secretions and body fluids like a living cosmic breath. This may be called the primary respiratory cycle of energy flow, with its own cranial rhythmic impulses as a physiological wireless energy response, like atomic current circuits. It is prior to and distinct from the regular respiration of the lungs' cycle of oxidation and pulse beat." (ET pp. 223-224)

Dr. Stone also spoke of a special relationship between energy, cerebrospinal fluid, the cranial rhythmic impulse or primary respiratory rate (PRR), structural balance, and health. "The cerebrospinal fluid is the liquid medium for life energy radiation, expansion and contraction. Where cerebrospinal fluid is present, there is life and healing with normal function. Where this primary and essential life force is not acting in the body, there is obstruction, spasm, or stagnation and pain, like gears which clash instead of meshing in their operation." (HB p.13) Cerebrospinal fluid is like a primordial ocean charged with life-giving energy and the PRR can be palpated as a wave which gives rise to the oceanic movement of cerebrospinal fluid throughout our body. Dr. Andrew Taylor Still, the founder of osteopathy, wrote, "The cerebrospinal fluid is the highest known element in the human body... He who is able to reason will see that this great river of life must be tapped and the withering field irrigated at once or the harvest of health is forever lost." *(Philosophy of Osteopathy)*

When learning cranial balancing, the practitioner must develop a sensitivity to the PRR and cerebrospinal fluid and then cultivate it over a lifetime of practice. With practice and persistence, the higher forms of cerebrospinal fluid pulsing with the PRR will be perceived. When the six-pointed star is aligned, the cerebrospinal fluid naturally heats up and rises from the physical body. During this process, the fluid transforms into finer and finer states of vapor, just as water evaporating from a lake transforms into a cloud. Therefore, a touch made with awareness is required both on and off the physical body.

The individual moves shown in the cranial and facial balancing protocols are based on cranial mechanics. Each bone is lifted into its correct position and gently held there until it aligns with the PRR. The movements necessary for a bone to align with the PRR are called, collectively, "unwinding." To begin the unwinding process, the practitioner first contacts the PRR and then tunes into a "place of resonance" which may be located anywhere from the surface to several feet or more off the body. Therefore the cranial moves are shown both on and off the body. The point of resonance is where your hands begin to vibrate and you sense energy pulsing between your fingertips and the cranium.

During cranial work, many things may happen on many different levels. Cranial balancing is much more than a physical process. You may come into contact with emotional states, thought forms, and even higher beings which are reflections of our perceptions from the realm of spirit, as you apply physical movements to assist in the healing process. As you work through these various levels, you will come to what is called a "still point"—the point where all movement ceases and the the cranial bones reorganize for better conduction of the PRR and cerebrospinal fluid.

Remember that energetic cranial balancing is a lifelong discipline. You must train yourself to tune into and listen to rhythms, fluid flows, and energetic changes. When properly performed, cranial balancing is an adventure into different states of consciousness. The cranial mechanism comes into balance and sends a wave of cerebrospinal fluid bringing your client back into the vibration of their ultrasonic core.

CRANIAL BALANCING PROTOCOL

1. Foot Cradle

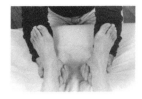

2. Sacrum Cradle

3. Balance East West Currents:

a. Pelvic Diaphragm

b. Respiratory Diaphragm

c. Thoracic Inlet

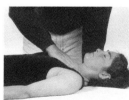

4. Tuning In

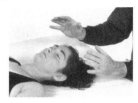

5. Cradle

6. Shelf

7. Temporal Unwinding

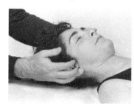

8. Ear Pull

9. Parietal Lift

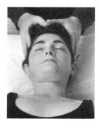

10. Frontal Lift

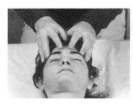

11. Sphenoid Lift

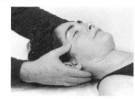

12. Angel's Blessing

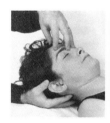

13. Front/Back Balance

14. Spinal Balance

Foot Cradle: Gently cradle the ankles with a slight inferior traction. Use your awareness to "feel" from the feet to the top of the head, noting any areas of tension/restriction or softness/openness. Tune into the energy wave of the Primary Respiratory Rate (PRR), gently allowing your energy to merge with it. Allow the wave to amplify and feel it flow from the feet to the head and back to the feet. Feel the entire body expand and contract.

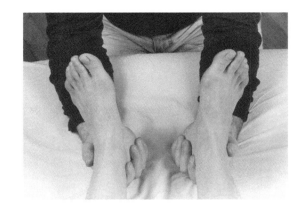

Sacrum Cradle: Place your right hand underneath the sacrum with a slight inferior traction. Place your left elbow and fingers on the outside of the anterior superior iliac spines as shown, and gently press them toward the center line of the body (medially) to decompress the sacroiliac joints and disengage the iliums from the sacrum. Allow the sacrum and iliums to unwind. Tune into the PRR and, using your awareness, sense the energy of the PRR throughout the pelvis and along the spine. Notice the quality of the sacral movement and any areas of openness or restriction.

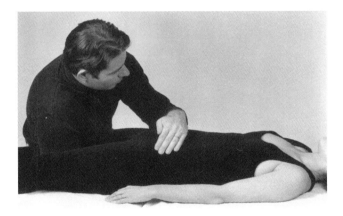

Variation: Place your hands outside the anterior superior iliac spines, gently press them toward the center line of the body, and allow the iliums to unwind.

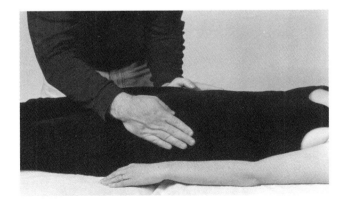

Balancing East West Currents

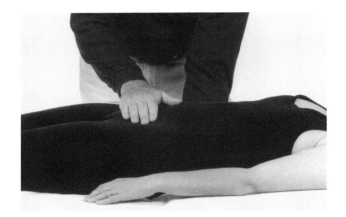

Pelvic Diaphragm: Place your left hand and right hand opposite one another on the lower back and abdomen at the level of the Water Chakra. Decompress the tissues of the pelvic diaphragm by pressing your hands together very gently until a resonant point of movement is felt. Tune into the energy. Allow the pressure between your hands to change as the energy moves. Your top hand may even come off the body at times. Stay here until you feel the tissues relax.

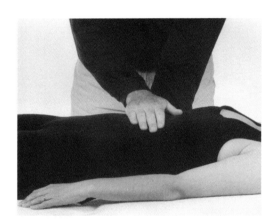

Respiratory Diaphragm: Place your left hand and right hand opposite one another on the midback and abdomen at the level of the Fire Chakra. Decompress the tissues of the respiratory diaphragm by pressing your hands together very gently until a resonant point of movement is felt. Tune into the energy. Allow the pressure between your hands to change as the energy moves. Stay here until you feel the tissues relax.

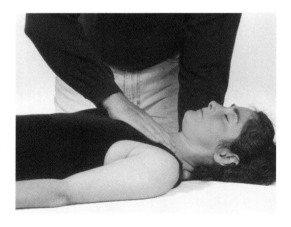

Thoracic Inlet: Place your left hand underneath the spine with your middle and index fingers around the spinous processes of the upper thoracic vertebrae. Place your right hand on the upper sternum below the clavicles at the level of the Heart Chakra with the thumb and first finger open and facing upward as shown. Decompress the tissues of the thoracic inlet by pressing your hands together very gently until a resonant point of movement is felt. Tune into the energy. Allow the pressure between your hands to change as the energy moves. Stay here until you feel the tissues relax.

Tuning In: Hold your hands one to twelve inches from the head. Move them around slowly and tune into the different energies around the cranium. Let your hands be soft and aware. Stay longer in areas which need your attention. The distance between your hands and the cranium may change as needed. At times you may even lightly touch the head.

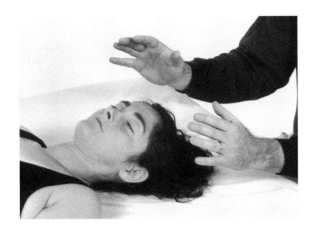

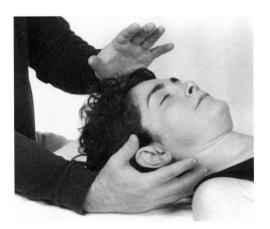

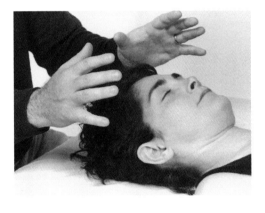

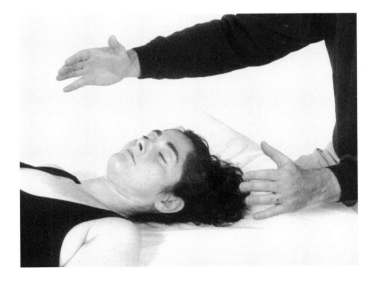

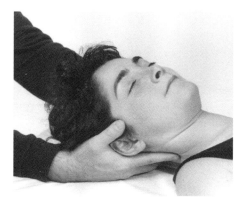

Cradle: Keep your hands soft and relaxed. Your index fingers go down the sides of the neck along the pathway of the Xth cranial nerve (which exits the skull just below the ear and runs down along the side of the neck). Your middle fingers cross at the occipital base and your thumbs rest by the ears. The head should be entirely cradled in your hands and not touching the table. Tune into the PRR. Feel the cranium expanding and contracting with it. You may also apply a slight superior traction and feel the energy of the PRR move down the whole body to the bottoms of the feet and return back up to the cranium.

Shelf: (Bk II Ch 49) With your forearms firmly supported by the table, cradle the head in your hands. Curl your fingers around the base of the skull and, with the pads of your fingers, feel for an area of soft tissue just below the occiput. With your fingers slightly curved back toward the top of the head, slip them into the soft tissue and lift the head off your hands with a gentle superior traction, disengaging the occiput from the atlas. Keep your hands relaxed yet firm and allow the head to drop back over your extended fingers. Imagine that you are making space between the atlas and occiput.

Temporal Unwinding: Place your index fingers lightly on the temperomandibular joints (TMJ) in front of the ears, your middle fingers just outside the external ear canals, and your fourth and fifth fingers on the mastoid processes behind the ears. Your thumbs make no contact and are neutral. Your hands should be open and "cupped," as if following the motion of the temporal bones which open like the gills of a fish. Visualize the gliding motion allowed by the temperoparietal (squamosal) sutures.

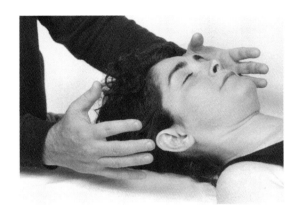

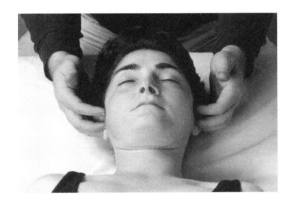

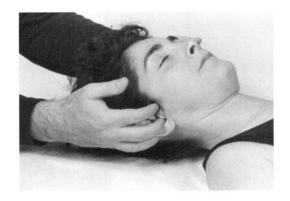

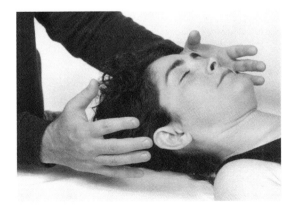

Ear Pull: Hold the ears gently as shown and pull on them as though they were a fine thread attached to a butterfly sleeping on a flower—you want to lift the butterfly 1/100 of an inch off the flower without waking it. Pull out and slightly down. Look for a fine vector of resistance and gently pull until it relaxes.

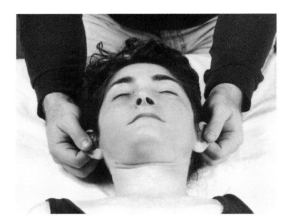

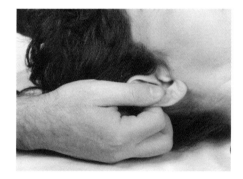

Frontal Lift: Place your fingers on the forehead as shown. Pretend that you have suction cups on the pads of your fingers. With your intention, lift the frontal bone in a forward direction (anteriorly). The motion is like tipping one's hat. Imagine you are lifting a fluffy white cloud into the sky and you must not allow your fingers to alter its shape.

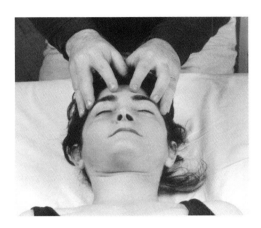

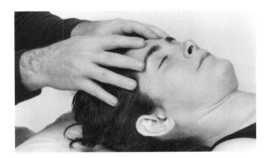

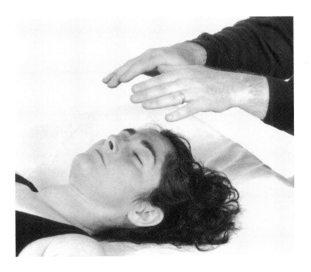

Parietal Lift: Place the finger pads of your first three fingers gently on the lateral aspects of the parietal bones just above the suture line. With your intention only, compress the bones medially just enough to sense a "firm handle," then gently lift upward (superiorly) and slightly outward (laterally) like a flower opening. Your thumbs may cross for stability and do not have to touch the head. Your little fingers may float free.

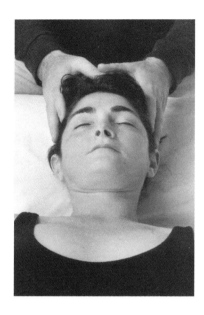

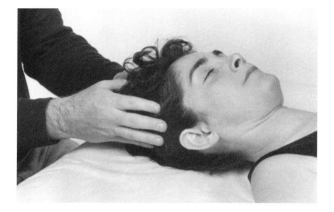

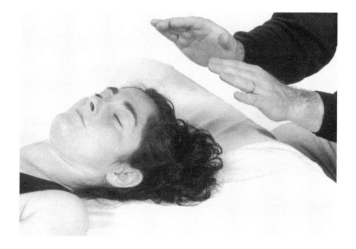

Sphenoid Lift: Place your thumbs gently on the greater wings of the sphenoid at the temples as shown. With your intention, lift forward (anteriorly) in the same direction as the frontal lift. Your fingers may contact the occiput for stabilization or float freely, not touching the head. Remember that the sphenoid is a transverse bone and your thumbs are contacting "wings." They want to fly. Be gentle. (See the Sphenoid Movement Evaluation section for a complete explanation of this move.)

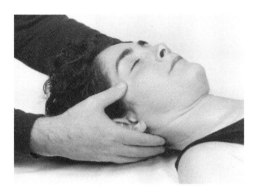

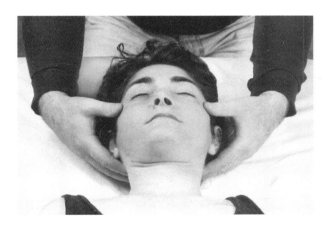

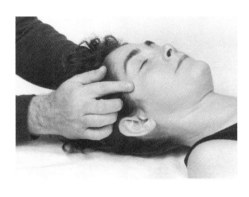

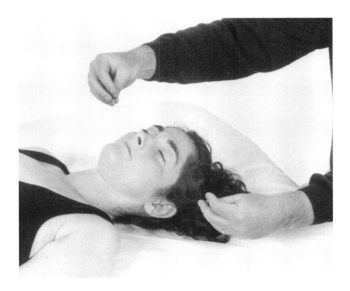

Angel's Blessing: Cup the occiput in your right hand creating a "V" between your third and fourth fingers. Place your left hand on the forehead with your third and fourth fingers along the upper nasals, the second and fifth fingers lightly touching the sides of the frontal bone, and your thumb resting just above the frontal fontanelle. Direct energy along the intracranial membranes, allowing it to "ping pong" between your hands.

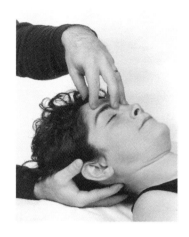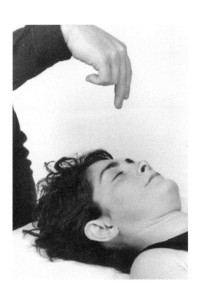

Front/Back Balance: Place the palm or fingertips of your left hand just off the frontal bone and the palm or fingertips of your right hand just off the occiput, creating a line through the sella turcica of the sphenoid and the occipital protuberance. Tune into the energy and find a resonant point; stay there until you perceive a "still point."

Spinal Balance: Place the fingertips of your left hand over the top of the head and the fingertips of your right hand just off the base of the coccyx as shown. Tune into the energy and find a resonant point; stay there until you perceive a "still point."

Notes

SPHENOID MOVEMENT EVALUATION INTRODUCTION

The sphenoid is the key to the cranium and the cranium is the key to the whole body or, as Dr. Stone says so often in his writings, "as above, so below." The exercises in this section utilize full body movement to help you learn the micro-movements of the sphenoid. These movements—on both a micro level, as sensed through cranial palpation, and a macro level, as observed and felt in the whole body—are keys to understanding the art of structural balancing.

The sphenoid should ideally have the full range of movement shown in the pictures. When these movements become restricted, this restriction is reflected through the whole body. For example, we can observe the shoulders and notice compression (the shoulders raised and the neck pressed downward, creating a "tight shell") as well as flexion/extension, sidebending (one shoulder higher than another), and/or torsion (the shoulders turned and rotated anteriorly or posteriorly). If the shoulders are observed in relationship to the neck above or diaphragm below, lateral and vertical relationships can also be seen. (Bk II Ch 11, 13; Bk IV Ch 3)

Ideally, the spine, as the central pillar of the body, should be flexible enough to move as necessary through the whole range of sphenoid movements. When we fail to meet a life challenge, the sphenoid and occiput are pressed together, creating a compressed, restricted or frozen movement pattern which is amplified throughout the body. When these patterns are repeated year after year, they may result in physical pain and symptoms which, over a period of time, may lead to illness.

SPHENOID MOVEMENT EVALUATION EXERCISES

The photographs in the first part of this section are designed to help you tune into and understand the importance of sphenoid movement in relation to whole body response, as well as the micro-movements of the sphenoid itself. To get the maximum value, try the following exercises:

Exercise #1

Look at the pictures showing the relationships between the sphenoid and occiput. If possible, you should a acquire a sphenoid and occiput and play with the relationships. A less expensive alternative would be using two objects, such as a pen and business card. Let the pen be the sphenoid, and the side of the business card the occiput. You can even cut the ends of the business card at 45° angles and punch a hole in the center to represent the foramen magnum. Move these objects through the full range of motion made by the sphenoid.

Exercise #2

When you have a clear sense of these movements, then exaggerate them with your whole body. Begin by assuming a restricted sphenoid pattern (one that is stuck in only one position). Remember that these patterns always involve some degree of compression. Pretend you have been in this pattern for many years. Ask yourself the following questions: How do I think when I am in this pattern? How do I experience the world? What would happen to my physical body after many years of being in this pattern? What emotions do I have while in this pattern? What do I need to express to get out of this pattern?

The next step is to experience a restricted sphenoid pattern in relationship to others. In groups of two or more, interact while using your whole body to assume various restricted sphenoid patterns. How does it feel to talk to someone in a different pattern than yours? How does it feel to talk to someone in the same pattern?

Exercise #3

Begin by rhythmically bouncing up and down. As you bounce, sidebend, torque, and go into flexion, extension, and lateral and vertical movements. Exaggerate these motions in a playful way. If you like, you may add music. Personally, I like to play Gene Autrey's "Back In The Saddle Again" and pretend that I am sitting in the sella turcica (literally, the "Turkish saddle") of the sphenoid. Bounce up and down and trot forward, allowing your body to move into the different positions. This is a lot of fun for a group to do together. Pretend you are riding through life and meeting different challenges as you change your position.

Micro-movements of the sphenoid amplified to whole body patterns:

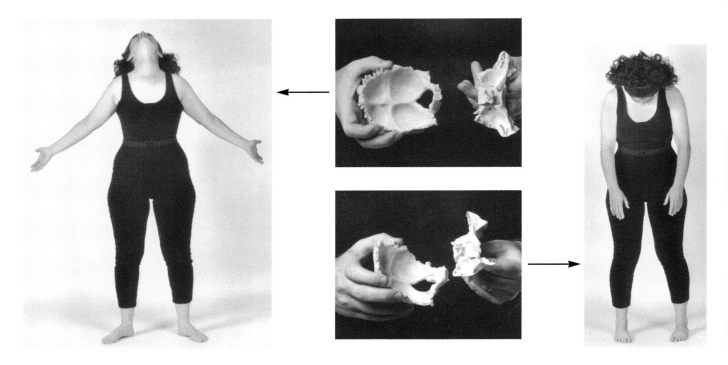

Flexion   Extension

Sidebending

Torsion

Lateral Motion

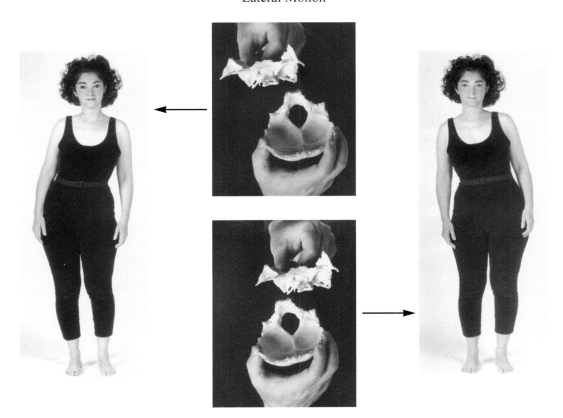

Vertical Motion

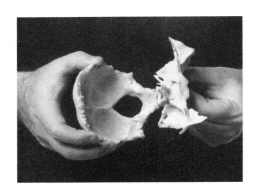

Compression

Micro-movements of the sphenoid amplified to whole body patterns in communication:

Sidebending/Flexion

Torsion/Vertical Motion in Flexion

Torsion/Sidebending

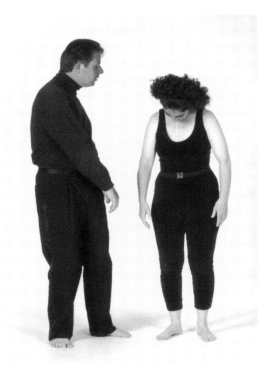

Torsion with Vertical Motion/Extension

Torsion with Vertical Motion/Sidebending

Torsion with Sidebending/Flexion

Flexion/Flexion

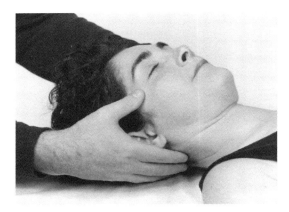
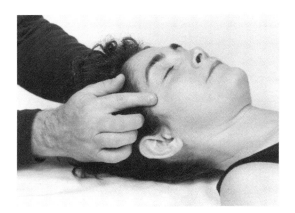

Sphenoid Balancing: Place your thumbs gently on the greater wings of the sphenoid at the temples as shown. With your intention, lift forward (anteriorly) in the same direction as the frontal lift. Your fingers may contact the occiput for stabilization or float freely, not touching the head. Remember that the sphenoid is a transverse bone and your thumbs are contacting "wings." They want to fly. Be gentle.

Step 1: Relax and let the sphenoid movements be amplified, so that your whole body moves with them. As you hold the sphenoid, you may feel yourself sidebending, compressing, etc. Listen without trying to correct anything.

Step 2: Tune into areas of greater motion and areas of restricted motion. Notice the relationship between the right and left sides.

Step 3: Allow the sphenoid to move freely into an area of greater motion. Follow this motion to its maximum limit and hold there for at least one minute.

Step 4: Relax and allow the sphenoid to move in the opposite, or restricted, direction. The sphenoid will now have more freedom of movement in this direction.

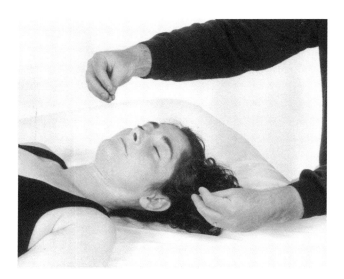

Notes

FACIAL BALANCING
INTRODUCTION

Our faces show our personalities, emotions, thoughts, moods, and hurts. We are recognized by others through the unique shape and quality of our faces. When you are happy, a smile changes your face. When you are sad or disappointed, your face changes again to reflect the feeling. When we do something wrong, we hide our faces, or hang our heads in shame. When we believe that our faces do not look good, we spend a lot of time with creams, razors, steams, wraps, mud, and may even see a plastic surgeon for face lifts, nose jobs, and wrinkle removal.

The ethmoid is the central bone of the face. It is located just behind the nasal bones and articulates directly with the sphenoid. When the sphenoid goes into flexion, the ethmoid rotates in a counterclockwise direction causing the face to open. When motion in the face is restricted, a "drag" is created on the occiput-sphenoid-ethmoid mechanism resulting in a distortion and compression of the entire cranial system.

The main causes of facial restriction are physical and psychological trauma. Physical trauma includes accidents involving facial injuries (*e.g.,* car, motorboat, airplane, sports accidents, etc.) which may result in broken noses, jaws, cracked teeth, and cuts. Physical trauma may also include invasive dental procedures such as root canals, extractions, braces, etc.

Psychological trauma includes shame, withholding feelings, lying, and physical, emotional or mental abuse. I have witnessed amazing facial changes occur when a client tells the truth. One day, a man who had come to me for headaches and vision problems spontaneously told me about an affair he was having. He said his wife did not know about it and he had been lying to her for over a year. As he talked, I could feel his temporal muscles begin to shake. Then he paused and, with great resolve, said that he would tell her. At that moment, his face went into contortions for several minutes and then relaxed. When I looked at him, his face was red, fuller, and beaming with energy. He looked like a new person. That night he was able to "face" his wife. Coincidentally, his headaches disappeared and his vision cleared.

When we hide our thoughts and feelings, it is called "withholding." When we withhold, we create a facial mask to hide the truth. Over a period of time, we begin to identify with our mask and restrict the honest expressive movements of our faces. Sometimes I refer to the ethmoid bone as the "ethical bone." When we tell the truth, the ethmoid naturally comes into balance, sending a wave of energy throughout the face and cranium. We see the world more clearly.

Work slowly and be aware of your client's vulnerability. Working with the face can be very revealing. The face is the center of our senses—smelling, tasting, seeing, and hearing. As the face comes into balance, new opportunities and openings quite naturally unfold.

FACIAL BALANCING PROTOCOL

1. Cradle

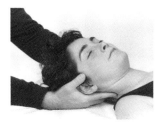

2. Shelf

3. Mandible Release

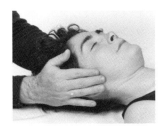

4. Nasal-Frontal Release

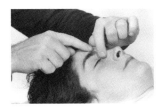

5. Ethmoid Release

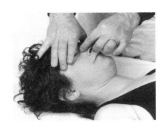

6. Maxilla Release

7. Palatine Release

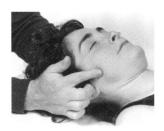

8. Vomer Release

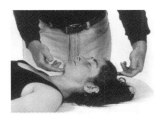

9. Teeth Unwinding

10. Hyoid Release

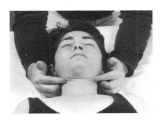

11. Facial Molding

12. Angel's Blessing

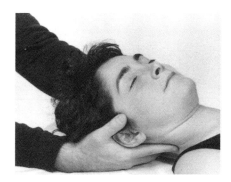 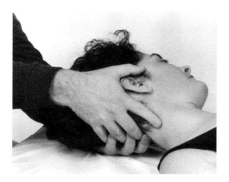

Cradle: Keep your hands soft and relaxed. Your index fingers go down the sides of the neck along the pathway of the Xth cranial nerve (which exits the skull just below the ear and runs down along the side of the neck). Your middle fingers cross at the occipital base and your thumbs rest by the ears. The head should be entirely cradled in your hands and not touching the table. Tune into the PRR. Feel the cranium expanding and contracting with it. You may also apply a slight superior traction and feel the energy of the PRR move down the whole body to the bottoms of the feet and return back up to the cranium.

Shelf: (Bk II Ch 49) With your forearms firmly supported by the table, cradle the head in your hands. Curl your fingers around the base of the skull and, with the pads of your fingers, feel for an area of soft tissue just below the occiput. With your fingers slightly curved back toward the top of the head, slip them into the soft tissue and lift the head off your hands with a gentle superior traction, disengaging the occiput from the atlas. Keep your hands relaxed yet firm and allow the head to drop back over your extended fingers. Imagine that you are making space between the atlas and occiput.

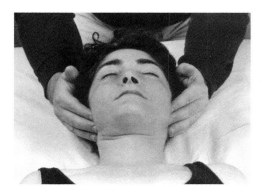

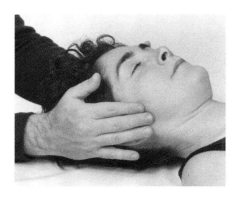

Mandible (TMJ) Release: Place your fingertips just above the angle of the mandible with a slight inferior traction. Your touch should be gentle, yet secure. Allow the temperomandibular joint (TMJ) to unwind.

Nasal-Frontal Release:
Place the tips of your index fingers as shown, so that there is a dual traction on the nasal and frontal bones. With the upper finger, pull diagonally with a slight superior traction. With the lower finger, pull with a slight inferior traction along the slope of the nose.

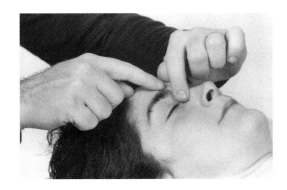

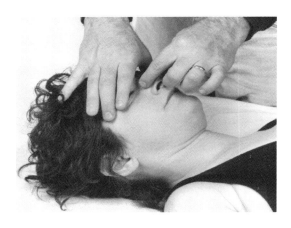

Ethmoid Release: Place the thumb and middle or index finger of your right hand on the greater wings of the sphenoid at the temples and apply a slight superior traction. Place the thumb and index finger of your left hand on either side of the nose just below the nasal bones and apply a slight downward traction along the slope of the nose. The traction you use should be more a matter of intention and direction of energy than a physical movement.

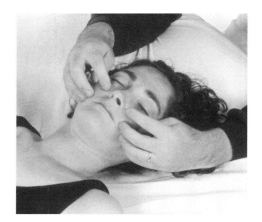
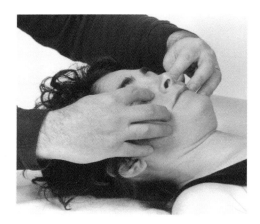

Maxilla Release: Place your fingers along the ridge of the cheeks as shown. With your intention, lift upward (superiorly) and outward (laterally).

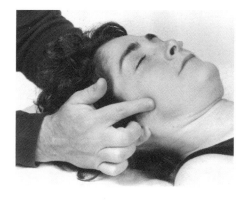

Palatine Release: Place your index fingers lightly on the soft tissue of the cheek in the notch made by the mandible and maxilla at the level of the upper back teeth. Press into the soft tissue just enough to feel a slight resistance and then direct the energy downward (inferiorly). Hold for several minutes, allowing the palatine bones to unwind.

Teeth Unwinding: Feel for the teeth through the soft tissue of the cheeks and around the mouth. Contact any tooth with your index finger and contact another tooth with your other index finger. For the upper teeth, direct the energy downward. For the lower teeth, direct the energy upward. You can make energy circuits between different teeth.

Vomer Release: Place the middle finger of your left hand on the frontal fontanelle and your other middle or index finger on the soft tissue beneath the chin as shown. Direct energy between your two fingers and imagine the vomer bone releasing.

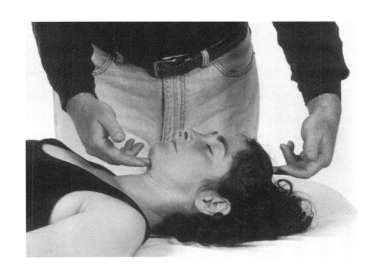

Hyoid Release: Place your index fingers on the tips of the hyoid bone as shown. Apply a very light pressure until you feel the bone unwinding. Hold for at least two minutes.

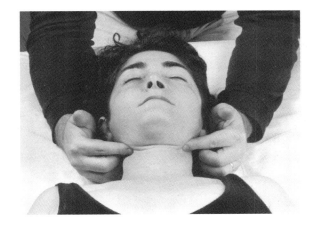

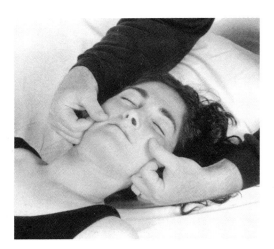

Facial Molding: Observe the symmetry of the face from different angles. Notice the highs and low areas. Pretend you are a sculptor and you can reshape the face. Place your hands over the face as shown in the first picture and hold this position for a minute or so. Then gradually, using your fingers and thumbs, press gently into the soft tissue in different directions based on your observations and palpation. Stop between strokes and observe. You may work this way for several minutes or even a whole session.

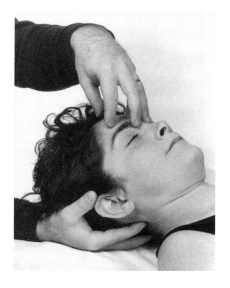

Angel's Blessing: Cup the occiput in your right hand creating a "V" between your third and fourth fingers. Place your left hand on the forehead with your third and fourth fingers along the upper nasals, the second and fifth fingers lightly touching the sides of the frontal bone, and your thumb resting just above the frontal fontanelle. Direct energy along the intracranial membranes, allowing it to "ping pong" between your hands.

SPINAL BALANCING
INTRODUCTION

Spinal balancing begins with an evaluation of the spine in relationship to the six-pointed star, or "six star," pattern and oval fields. This evaluation will give a direction and set the tone for each move of the protocol. The goal is to use structural bodywork to bring the body back into alignment with the six star pattern and create a horizontal and vertical symmetry among the oval fields.

The spine forms the central core of the body. Energetically, the spine is called the "Tree of Life" and, like a tree, it is built to be flexible and bend with the weather. Dr. Stone says that "obstacles are God's design to make man with a spine." He is implying that the challenges of everyday living, like the changing weather, require spinal flexibility and firmness. Sometimes we have to bend with the energy and other times we must root ourselves in the earth and take a clear stand. When we fail to adopt the correct spinal posture, words like "spineless" are used to describe our behavior.

Failing to meet a life challenge causes the spine—by way of the oval fields and six star pattern—to go out of alignment. For example, if someone is holding back their expression of Fire, we may observe a contracted diaphragm, small lower rib cage, and an anterior thoracic curve in the area of the Fire chakra. The Fire oval may appear small and contracted compared to the Air oval above and Earth oval below. This may lead, over a period of time, to digestive problems, gall bladder or liver disorders, stomach upset or ulcers.

The sacrum forms the base of the spine. The word sacrum means "sacred bone." Dr. Stone thought so much of the sacrum that he wrote an entire book about it, appropriately titled *The Mysterious Sacrum*. The position and flexibility of the sacrum between the iliums creates a foundation upon which the spine and cranium rest. Inside the sacrum, the kundalini sleeps like a seed waiting to be watered.

The lumbar vertebrae form the trunk of the spinal tree which rises upwards to the cranium. The cranium can be seen as a flower which, having received its nourishment from the challenges of life, opens to the light of Spirit. When this happens, the sphenoid lifts up like a butterfly and brings the nectar of cerebrospinal fluid back up to Spirit. When the spine is balanced from the sacrum to the top of the head, heaven and earth meet.

SPINAL BALANCING PROTOCOL

1. Cradle

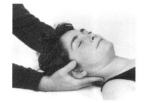

2. Sidebending Stretch Release

3. North Pole Stretch with Traction

4. North Pole Stretch with Rotation

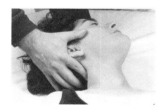

5. Foramen Magnum Release

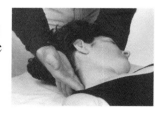

6. Connective Tissue Release of Cervical and Upper Thoracic Spine

7. Crossover Lift

8. Shelf

9. Sacrum Cradle

10. L5/S1 Release

(Face Down)

11. "S" Technique along Spine

12. Pelvic & Hip Adjustments

13. Cervical & Upper Thoracic Release

14. Directional Force Techniques

15. Spinal Muscle & Rib Head Release

(Side)

16. Pelvis Rock

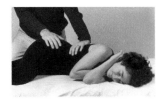

17. Lower Back Stretch Release

18. Sacrum Release

19. Rotational Twist

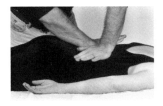

20. Sacral Balancing

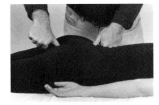

21. Spinal Harmonics

22. Spinal Chakra Balancing

(Sitting)

23. North Pole Stretch

24. North Pole Stretch with Rotation

25. Crossover Lift

26. Shelf

27. Mid-Thoracic Stretch

28. Lower Thoracic & Lumbar Stretch

Cradle: Keep your hands soft and relaxed. Your index fingers go down the sides of the neck, your middle fingers cross at the occipital base, and your thumbs rest by the ears. The head should be entirely cradled in your hands and not touching the table. Apply a gentle, almost imperceptible, superior traction and allow your awareness to move down the spine to the tip of the coccyx, feeling any areas of tension. If you have taken basic cranial class, tune into the primary respiratory rhythm. [BW: I.B4]

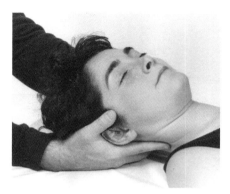
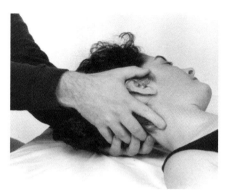

Sidebending Stretch Release: Place your left hand on the top of the left shoulder and your right hand under the base of the occiput. Firmly hold the left side of the occiput while gently pulling the neck toward the right so that the right ear moves toward the right shoulder. As you stretch, stabilize the left shoulder; do not allow it to come up. Repeat on the other side. [preparation for BW: V.G1d]

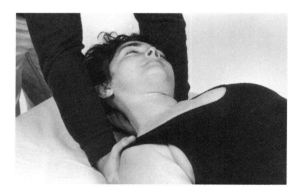

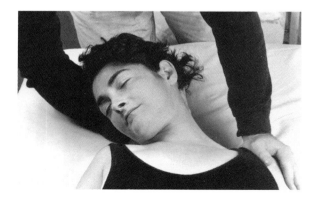

North Pole Stretch with Traction:
(Bk II Ch 42; Bk III Ch 25; Bk IV Ch 7; Bk V pp. 69-70)
Cradle the head in your hands, firmly holding the occipital base with your
index fingers and applying a gentle superior traction. Ask your client to inhale
deeply and, as they exhale, increase the traction. As you pull, gently shake the
neck and allow your awareness to scan the entire spine. [BW: II.A7]

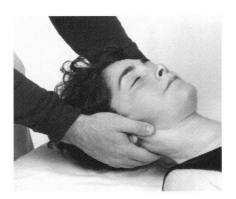 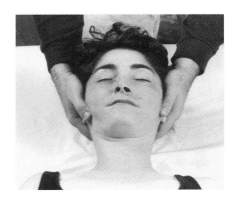

North Pole Stretch with Rotation: After doing the North Pole Stretch with Traction,
continue to hold the head and occipital base with your right hand. Maintain a slight
superior traction and rotate the head to the right, allowing your left hand to turn as
shown, until a gentle stretch is felt. Repeat on the opposite side. [preparation for
BW: V.G1d]

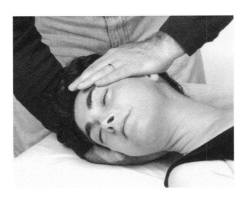 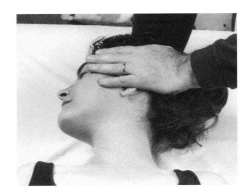

Foramen Magnum Release: (Bk II Ch 39, 40) Grasp the head at the occipital base with both hands. Sidebend the neck toward the right and then rotate the head upward toward the left. Ask your client to take a deep breath and stretch as they breathe out. Hold your position as you ask them to take another deep breath and stretch a little further as they breathe out. Work gently and slowly until you are able to feel the stretch. Repeat on the opposite side. [BW: V.G1d]

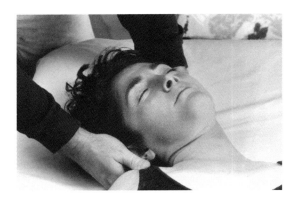
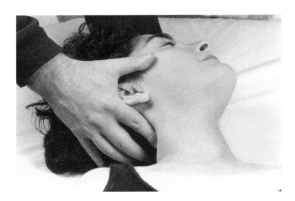

Sidebend Right   Rotate Left

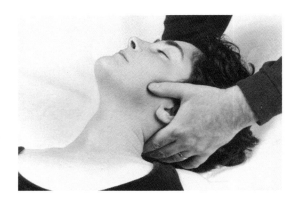
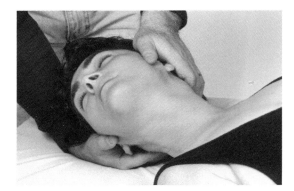

Foramen Magnum Release seen from different angles

Connective Tissue Release of the Cervical & Upper Thoracic Spine: (Bk II, Ch 41, Fig.1) Side bend the neck to one side and, with your free hand, press into the muscle tissue along the side of the neck (trapezius, scalenes) until you feel a slight resistance. Beginning just below the occiput, allow your hand to move slowly down toward the shoulders, adjusting your pressure to stay at the edge of any resistance you encounter. To be effective, this move should be done slowly and with awareness. It should feel as if you are riding a wave up and down. You may do it several times from different starting points. Do both sides.

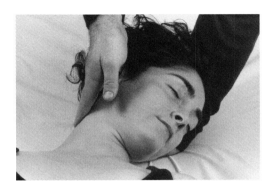
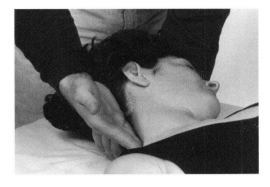

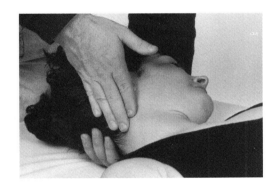

Crossover Lift and Crossover Lift with Upper Thoracic Release: (Bk II Ch 50) Place your left hand on the right shoulder with the occipital base supported on your forearm as shown. For the crossover lift, place your right hand on the left shoulder with your right arm beneath your left arm. Ask your client to take a deep breath and, as they exhale, lift the head forward toward the chest with your forearms while stabilizing the shoulders with your hands. For the connective tissue release of the upper thoracics, crossover with only one arm. Lift the head slightly and place your free hand along the side of the upper thoracic spine on that side. Ask your client to take a deep breath and, as they exhale, lift the head forward toward the chest with your forearm while simultaneously working your way up the tissue along the side of the spine with your fingertips. [BW: V.E2b]

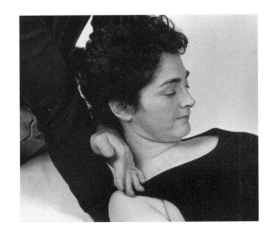

Shelf: (Bk II Ch 49) With your forearms firmly supported by the table, cradle the head in your hands. Curl your fingers around the base of the skull and, with the pads of your fingers, feel for an area of soft tissue just below the occiput. With your fingers slightly curved back toward the top of the head, slip them into the soft tissue and lift the head off your hands with a gentle superior traction, disengaging the occiput from the atlas. Keep your hands relaxed yet firm and allow the head to drop back over your extended fingers. Imagine that you are making space between the atlas and occiput.

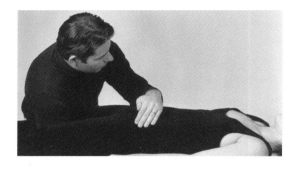

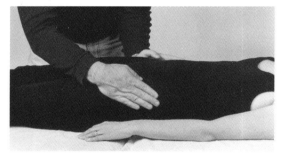

Sacrum Cradle: Place your right hand underneath the sacrum with a slight inferior traction. Place your left elbow and fingers on the outside of the anterior superior iliac spines as shown, and gently press them toward the center line of the body (medially) to decompress the sacroiliac joints and disengage the iliums from the sacrum. Allow the sacrum and iliums to unwind. Tune into the PRR and, using your awareness, sense the energy of the PRR throughout the pelvis and along the spine. Notice the quality of the sacral movement and any areas of openness or restriction.

Variation: Place your hands outside the anterior superior iliac spines, gently press them toward the center line of the body, and allow the iliums to unwind.

S1/L5 Release: (HB pp. 58) Make a fist with your right hand and place it as shown just above the superior border of the sacrum. The spinous processes of the lower lumbars should fit into the gap between your curled fingers and the heel of your hand. Decompress the iliums and hold until you feel the lower back relax.

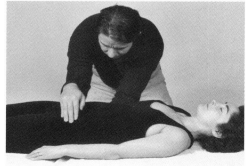

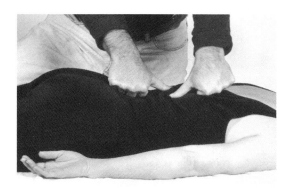

"S" Technique, or Walking the Kundalini: (Bk II Ch 24, Fig. 3) Begin by placing your right thumb on the left side of the spine and your left thumb on the right side of the spine. Press into the soft tissue until you feel your thumbs "grip" the tissue and then simultaneously push upward (superiorly) with your right thumb and downward (inferiorly) with your left thumb. Begin at the base of the spine and alternate your thumbs from side to side, as you walk up the spine. [BW: V.B1b]

In general, the "S" technique has many variations and can be used anywhere to loosen or reduce soft tissue spasm. For example, your thumbs may be placed further apart creating large S's, you can use your hands or forearms and create "S" stretches, or you can bring your thumbs closer together and do one side of the spine at a time.

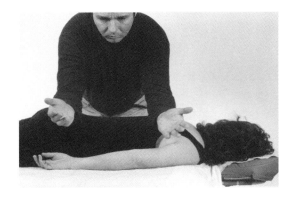

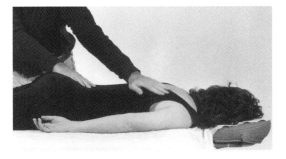

Variation of "S" Technique using forearms across spine: Move your right forearm forward (away from your body) and your left forearm back, creating an "S" stretch. Then move your forearms in the opposite directions.

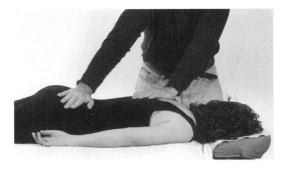

Variation of "S" Technique using hands: Place your right hand on the right side of the sacrum and your left hand over the scapula. Your left hand pulls and your right hand pushes along the diagonal between your hands. Stretch both sides.

Pelvic & Hip Adjustments for Tender Areas in the Gluteus Region: (Bk II Ch 34, Fig. 1-3; Bk III Ch 20)
Ask your client to lie down on their side with the head supported. Contact the head of the femur with your thumb, pointing it in the direction of the lines of tension found in the fibers of the gluteus muscles. Adjust the position of the leg from superior to inferior based on the lines of tension you feel. Your other hand may contact the heel, ankle, or sacrum. You may work down the tension line with your thumb or palm. [BW: V.C3a]

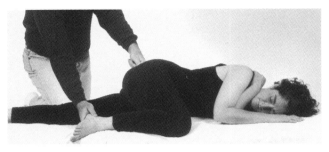

Leg placed superiorly with a specific contact
on an outside ankle point

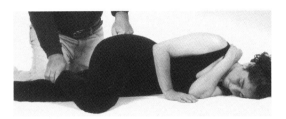

Leg placed inferiorly with general contact
on the ankle

Working the line of tension along the glutei
with the "S" technique

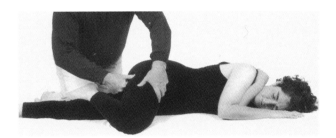

Working the line of tension along the leg
with the "S" technique

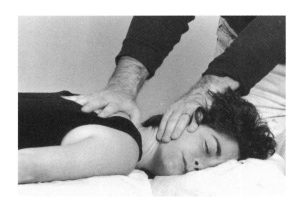

Cervical and Upper Thoracic Release: (Bk II Ch 41, Fig. 1)
With the head turned to the right side, place your left hand over base of the cranium and the right hand along the upper thoracic vertebrae as shown. Gently rotate the back of the cranium to the left (toward the table) while pressing downward (inferiorly) along the soft tissue to the right of the thoracic spine. Do both sides. [BW: V.I1a & V.F1a]

Directional Force Applied to Energy Blocks: (Bk II Ch 22) Locate a point of tension on either side of the spine. Place your elbow or thumbs on the point and gradually press into it. Press in a relaxed way using the weight of your entire body. As you feel the tissues release, change the direction of your pressure. This move should be painless. The more relaxed you are, the deeper you will be able to press while maintaining awareness. Hold each move until you feel the tissues relax and come to a place of stillness. [BW: V.B3a]

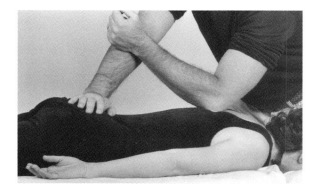

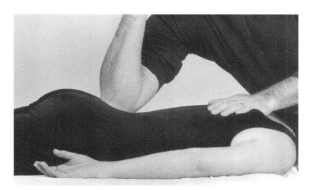

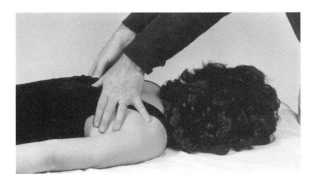
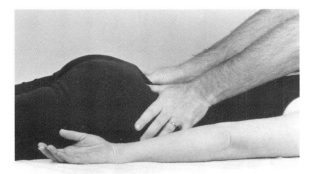

Release Spinal Muscles and Rib Heads: (Bk II Ch 41, Fig. 2; Ch 57, Fig. 4) Place your thumbs on the posterior rib heads and press downward (inferiorly) with either a slight thrust and or a steady pressure. The same technique may be used over the scapula, sacrum, or anywhere along the spine to release muscle spasm. [BW: V.E1a]

Pelvis Rock: (Bk II Ch 35) Ask your client to lie down on their side with the head supported. The bottom leg should be straight and the top leg bent as shown. You may adjust the angle of the top leg to stretch different areas of the lower back. You may also choose to let the top leg fall over the side of the table for even more stretch. Place your lower hand or forearm on the pelvis and your upper hand or forearm on or just below the shoulder. Stretch and rock, alternating directional pressure between the shoulder and pelvis. Try different angles. [BW: I.A3]

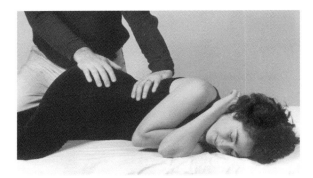
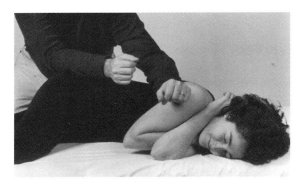

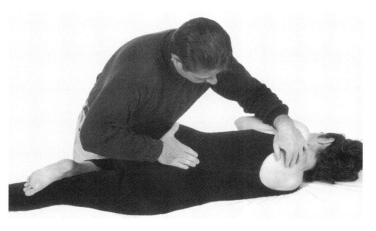

Lower Back Stretch Release:
(Bk II Ch 34, Fig. 4; Bk V pp. 29-30) Have your client lie on their side with the lower leg straight and the upper leg bent as shown. Place your lower hand on the lower back anywhere from L5-L1 and your upper hand or forearm on or just below the shoulder. You can stretch by pushing the shoulder posteriorly and the lower back anteriorly. You may also stretch while doing a connective tissue release by pressing the fingers of your lower hand into the tissues along the spine and sliding them slowly upward. Be careful not to use excessive force. [BW: V.Da]

Sacrum Release: (EES Ch 22) Hold the foot securely underneath one of your arms as shown. Find a sensitive point on the outer ankle and press into it with your middle finger as you move the foot toward the buttocks (superiorly), flexing the knee. Then straighten the leg while pressing into a sensitive point near the center of the hip with the thumb of your other hand. Do this three to ten times, varying the pumping rhythm and the angle of the leg. You may also grip both legs together and rotate them from side to side while pressing into the muscles of the hip. [BW: V.H1d]

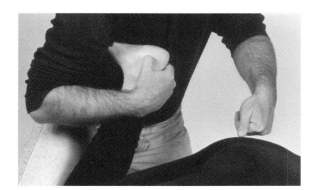
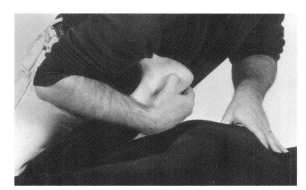

Rotational Twist: (Bk III Ch 18) Place the heels of your hands in opposite directions along the side of the spine as shown. Press down into the tissues and simultaneously rotate your hands in a clockwise direction approximately 90 degrees. You should not thrust, but you may give a slight impulse or just hold a steady, firm contact. This may be done anywhere on the middle to lower thoracic spine. [BW: I.B1]

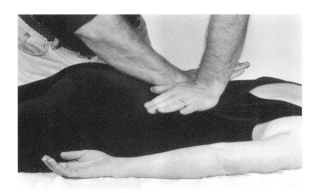

Sacral Balancing: (Bk IV Ch 4) Place your hand over the sacrum and tune into its movements. Based on your palpation, hold superior/inferior diagonal contacts through the sacrum. The angles may be adjusted as you feel the energy move. The pressure may be satvic, rajasic, or tamasic. You may use the high and low spinal side/long leg relationship as a guide or you may place your hands on the occiput and sacrum and palpate for guidance. [BW: V.H1a]

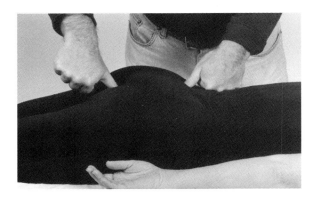
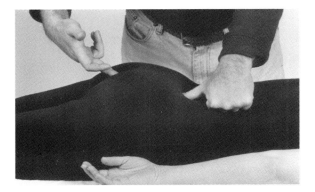

Spinal Harmonics: (Bk V Ch 2, 15) There are several ways to facilitate spinal harmonic balancing. You may do them individually or combine them as you choose. Begin by placing your hand on the sacrum and occiput as shown. Feel for a wave traveling through the spine as your client breathes in and out. Note any areas along the spine where the wave seems to be restricted. [BW: V.B2b]

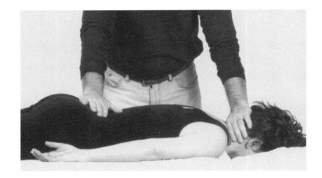
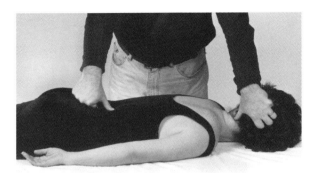

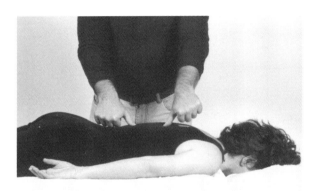

1. Place your left thumb on the left transverse process one vertebra above the restricted area and your right thumb on the right transverse process one vertebra below the restricted area, creating a diagonal across the spine. Hold satvically for a few moments and then switch the diagonal to the other side and hold satvically until you feel the restriction ease. (Bk V p. 22)

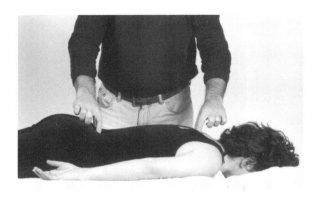

2. Place your thumb and index finger over the transverse processes of the restricted vertebra. Place your other thumb and index finger over the transverse processes of a harmonically-related vertebra. Satvically hold until you feel the restriction ease.

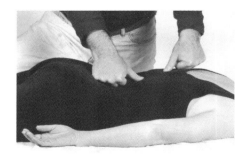

3. Create a diagonal between harmonically-related vertebrae by placing one thumb on the left or right side of the restricted vertebra and the other thumb on the opposite side of a harmonically-related vertebra. Hold satvically until you feel the restriction ease.

SPINAL HARMONICS

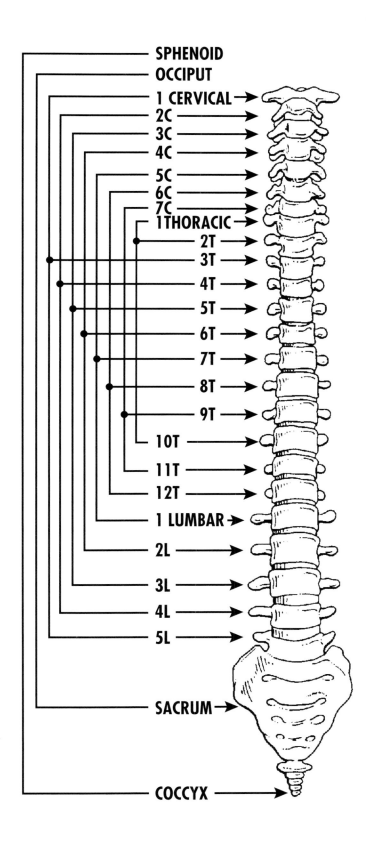

SPHENOID
OCCIPUT
1 CERVICAL
2C
3C
4C
5C
6C
7C
1 THORACIC
2T
3T
4T
5T
6T
7T
8T
9T
10T
11T
12T
1 LUMBAR
2L
3L
4L
5L
SACRUM
COCCYX

Spinal Chakra Balancing: (Bk V p. 73) For Ether, place your left hand comfortably on the back of the occiput as shown. For Earth, place your right hand, palm up, with the center knuckle touching the tip of the coccyx. The left hand remains satvic. With your right hand rock three to ten times, stop for a moment, and then rock again. For Water, place your right hand, palm down, at the level of the S1/L5 vertebrae as shown. Rock back and forth three to ten times, stop for a moment, and then rock again. For Fire, slide your right hand up to the mid-spine (T11/12). Rock back and forth three to ten times, stop for a moment, and then rock again. For Air, slide your right hand upward to the area between the shoulder blades (T5). Rock back and forth three to ten times, stop for a moment, and then rock again. When you are done, lift your hands off the body slowly. [BW: I.B5]

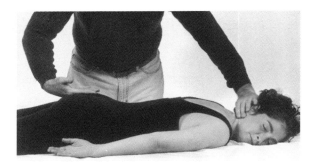

Earth

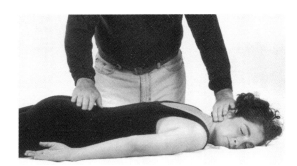

Water

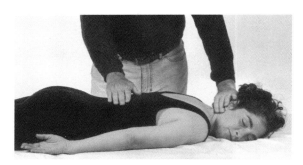

Fire

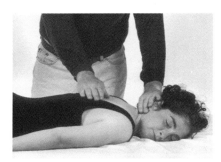

Air

Sitting North Pole Stretch:
(Bk II Ch 42; Bk III Ch 25; Bk IV, Ch 7; Bk V pp. 69-70)
Allow your client's body to rest comfortably against yours. Place your hands as shown, with your thumbs along the occipital base. Ask your client to take a deep breath as you lift the head upward to its maximum extension. You should take a deep breath with them. Holding the head in this exact spot, ask your client to exhale slowly, making a long, deep "aah" sound, as their body drops downward. Do this one to three times. [BW: II.A7; V.G1a]

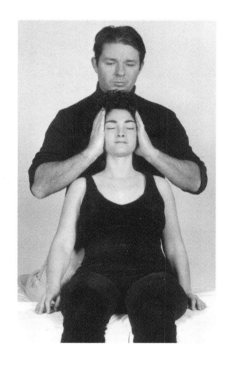

Sitting North Pole Stretch with Rotation: Stabilize the shoulder with one hand as shown so that it does not move forward (anteriorly) during the stretch. Place your other hand under the occiput and along the side of the head. Ask your client to rest comfortably against your body and take a deep breath. Breathe in as your client breathes in, lift upward at the occiput and, with the palm of your hand, rotate the head as shown. On the exhale, keep the head suspended and allow the neck to stretch. Do both sides.

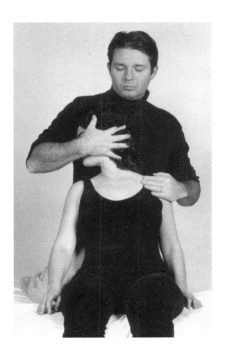
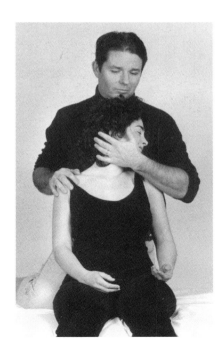

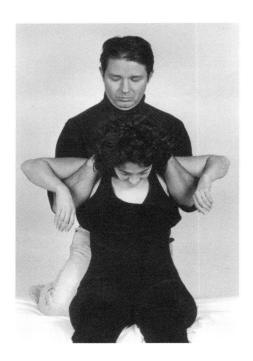

Sitting Crossover Lift: (Bk II Ch 50) Place your arms underneath your client's shoulders and interlace your hands behind the occiput as shown. Ask your client to lean back onto your body and take a deep breath as you slowly lift them upward and back (posteriorly) to their maximum extension. At the top of the extension, use your chest to give a slight forward thrust on their upper thoracic spine or gently shake them from side to side. As they exhale, ask them to make sounds. [BW: V.E2b]

Sitting Shelf: (Bk II Ch 49) Place your thumb and index finger along the occipital base. Place your other hand on the forehead as shown and gently press the head in a posterior direction. Keep your hand at the occiput firm; do not allow it to move backward with the head. Let the head drop back gradually and be aware of tissue changes along the occiput. [BW: V.G1e]

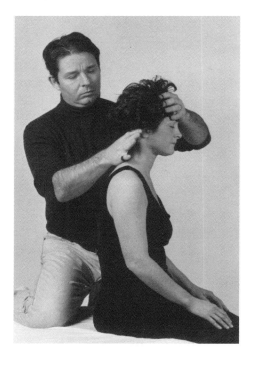

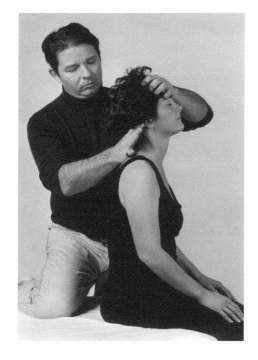

Spinal Stretch Releases
[BW: V.E1b, 2a]

Mid-Thoracic Stretch: (Bk II Ch 45) Grasp the left shoulder as shown, allowing your client's body to rest comfortably on yours. Place the heel of your left palm along the left side of the spine anywhere between T5-T10. With your right hand, simultaneously lift and turn the torso to the right while pushing along the twisting line with your left hand. Do both sides. If appropriate, ask your client to make sounds. [BW: II.A4]

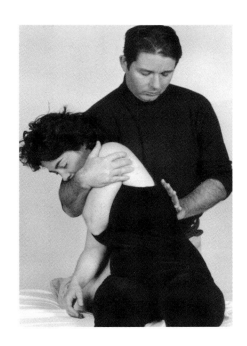

Lower Thoracic & Lumbar Stretch: (EES Ch 23, Fig. 1) Place your right arm under the right shoulder and around the back of the neck to stabilize it. Rotate your client's torso to the right, back and downward, supporting them with your body and left hand as shown. How far back and downward you allow your client to go and the angle of rotation will determine the vertebral areas affected. The higher the client is when they fall backward, the higher the vertebral area that is effected.

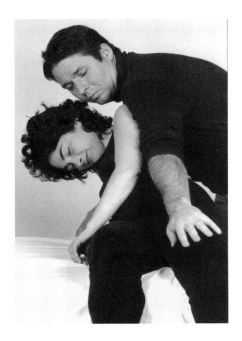

STRUCTURAL EVALUATION

I. Visual Observation
(Bk I Ch 7; Bk II Ch 11, 13; Bk III Ch 10, 11)
[EV: 4.a, b, c, 1, 2, 3, 4, 5, a, b; 5.]

A. Stand four to six feet behind your client; then stand in front of your client and observe the following:

1. The relationship between the neck and shoulders, e.g., are the shoulders raised, causing the neck to appear sandwiched between them? Is the neck tilted to one side?

2. Is one shoulder higher than the other?

3. The relationship between the torso and the pelvis, e.g., is the torso tilted to the left or right? Is the torso torqued to the left or right?

4. The relationship between the shoulders, torso, and pelvis, e.g., are the shoulders sidebending to the right and the pelvis sidebending to the left? How is the torso compensating?

5. How do the feet relate to the floor? Are they flat, curved inward or outward, one outward and the other inward, tilted to the midline, etc.?

6. The relationship between the pelvis, legs, and feet, e.g., is one leg turned outward or inward? Does one side of the pelvis appear higher, causing one leg to appear longer? Is there any sidebending, torsion, or lateral motion?

7. The relationship between spinal curvatures and oval fields:

   a. How are the fields aligned? Does one field appear to be out of alignment with the field above or below?

   b. How are the fields proportioned and shaped? Is one field larger than another? Does a field appear to have an "inharmonic shape"?

8. Allowing your own body to take the shape of your client's body, note your feelings, intuitions, and impressions.

B. Standing four to six feet to the side of your client, observe the following from both sides and note any differences:

1. Your client's overall posture from head to toe.

2. The relationship between your client's neck and shoulders, e.g., do they appear to be "stuck out" or "held in"? Does the neck appear to be "hiding" between the shoulders?

3. The relationship between the pelvis and the torso: Note any anterior or posterior lateral motion. Note any sidebending or torsion.

4. How do the feet relate to the floor?

5. The relationship between the pelvis, legs, and feet, e.g., are the knees locked? Do the thighs protrude over the knees or are they held back? Do the feet seem large or small in comparison to the legs and pelvis? Is the pelvis lifted?

6. The relationship between the curves of the spine and oval fields:

   a. How are the fields aligned? Does one field protrude? Is another field held back?

   b. How are the fields proportioned? Does one field seem too large in comparison to another, e.g., a barrel chest and small pelvis or a small chest and large pelvis?

7. Allowing your body to take the shape of your client's body, note your feelings, intuitions, and impressions.

II. Palpation
(Bk IV Ch 3; Bk V Ch 2) [EV: 5, 6, 7]

A. Locate spinal landmarks:

1. C2: With your client lying supine in a face cradle, press lightly into the center of the spine, just below the occiput. The first bump will be the spinous process of C2.

2. C7: With your client lying supine in a face cradle, feel for the most protuding vertebra at the base of the neck. Place your finger on the spinous process and have your client lift their head. If the vetrebra above "disappears" and the vertebra you are palpating "stays," you are on C7. The vertebra below is T1.

3. T7: With your client lying supine in a face cradle, feel for the bottom of the shoulder blades (inferior border of the scapula). Draw a line between these points. The line crosses T7.

4. T12: With your client lying supine in a face cradle, feel for the bottom of the rib cage and trace the edge of the lowest rib; where it inserts into the spine is T12.

5. L4-5: With your client lying supine in a face cradle, feel for the top of the hips (superior iliac crests). Draw a line from crest to crest. The line crosses the L4-5 space.

B. Identify the long and short leg:

1. With your client lying face up, cup the heels of the feet. Lift and gently shake them from side to side with a slight inferior pull and then place them back on the table. Observe the horizontal relationship between the heels, i.e., notice if one leg appears longer than the other.

2. Cradle the ankles and apply a slight inferior traction. Close your eyes and tune into the fascia from the feet to the head. Note any areas of contraction, openness, tightness, bunching, etc. Note if one leg feels longer than the other. To develop your palpation skills, place a sheet over a smooth table. Place one or two objects on the sheet. Close your eyes and gently pull as you did on the ankles. Feel for the resistance of the objects.

C. Place the palm of your left hand on the occiput and the palm of your right hand over the sacrum. Tune into your client's breathing and feel the wave of breath through the spine. Note any areas of restriction.

D. Hold your hands one inch or less over the spine. Move your hands up and down along the spine and feel for any temperature changes. Note the quality of the changes and in which areas they occur.

E. Touch each spinous process with the index finger of your left hand and rock each vertebra up and down. Notice any sensitivity.

F. Palpate along the spine with a lateral rocking motion, identifying areas of restriction and mobility.

G. Relate your findings to the oval fields and spinal chakras.

ABOUT ANATOMY

A knowledge of musculoskeletal anatomy is necessary for structural evaluation and for utilizing Dr. Stone's origin/insertion release techniques (Bk II Ch 32) [BW: V.B1a]. When you observe and palpate, it helps to know which muscles and muscle groups are involved in a high shoulder, torqued spine, turned-in foot, etc. Structural anatomical knowledge is best learned through a three dimensional experience.

The Maniken Anatomiken system is an excellent structural learning model. It is available through Zahourek Systems, Inc., 38 Mercer Street, Jersey City, NJ 07302; tel: 201-432-9204. The Maniken, shown in the picture on p. 218, is a specially designed skeleton model made for shaping, building, and attaching clay muscles in both flexion and extension positions. (Note: If you find this model too expensive, you can purchase a plastic skeleton and clay at a hobby store and build different muscle groups.)

It works well with the *Atlas of the Skeletal Muscles* by Robert J. Stone and Judith A. Stone, Wm. C. Brown Publishers, Dubuque, IA. A complement to building the Maniken is an excellent experiential anatomy book, *Body Stories: A Guide to Experiential Anatomy* by Andrea Olsen, Station Hill Press, Barrytown, NY. And, for those who want more specific evaluation skills, I recommend *Physical Examination of the Spine and Extremeties* by Stanley Hopenfeld, Appleton-Century-Crofts, Norwalk, CT.

Notes

SPECIAL PROTOCOLS
INTRODUCTION

The protocols presented in this section are based on the application of Polarity principles to different systems of the body, e.g., the nervous system, digestive system, lymphatic system, circulatory system, and genito-urinary system.

In his writings, Dr. Stone refers to many specific treatments for healing these systems and the symptoms which signal their imbalance such as diarrhea, constipation, sciatica, heart problems, headaches, anxiety, hemorrhoids, ulcers, etc. In using these treatments it is important to remember that they have originated from an energetic understanding and evaluation based on Polarity principles. To assume that one can press a point or connect a circuit and digestion will improve or an ulcer will go away is called "cookbook thinking." This type of thinking completely by passes the principles of Polarity and limits the practitioner's ability to evaluate the unique needs of their clients.

Learning these moves should involve making connections between anatomy and physiology, energetic anatomy, and Polarity principles. When Dr. Stone says a certain manipulation will help constipation, you should ask yourself how Dr. Stone made this discovery. Trace his reasoning from Polarity principle through anatomy to the body system he is treating. Ask yourself how he evaluated his clients to create these treatments and what elements and/or structural qualities are present.

Many of the moves in these protocols can be used to form a complete session. For example, the lymphatic moves can be expanded into a full body lymphatic session or can be used on only part of the body to stimulate lymphatic flow. The Fire Spiral can include many points or can be limited to only a few. The Five Star moves can be expanded into a full session using many reflex circuits and stretches to bring the body into alignment with the five star pattern.

The following special protocols complete this text because they represent an initiation into the creative process of Polarity practice. By working with them, you will develop an ability to trace the energy in different systems of the body and create specific results.

However, always remember that Polarity first balances elemental energies, creating the environment which can allow symptoms to disappear. Dr. Stone tells us that true healing is a return to our ultrasonic core. When the root is nourished, the tree of life flourishes.

NERVOUS SYSTEM AND FIVE STAR PROTOCOL

1. Balance Sacrum and Occiput

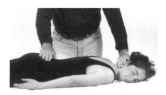

2. Scapula Release

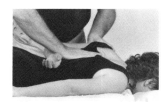

3. Release Shoulder Muscles and Rib Heads

4. Coccyx/Sphenoid Balance

5. Balance Perineum and Neck

6. Balance Perineum and Shoulders, Hips, Knees, Elbows, and Ankles

7. Balance Sensory Reflexes

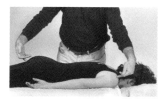

8. Cradle

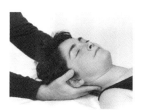

9. Psoas Release

10. Five Star Balance

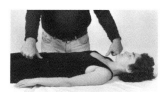

11. Sitting Scapula Release

12. Sitting Crossover Lift

13. Sitting Spinal Stretch for Gas Release

14. Sitting North Pole Stretch

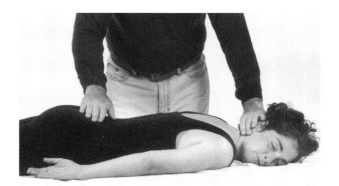

Balance Sacrum and Occiput: (Bk V Ch 17, Fig. 1) Place the thumb of one hand on the side of the occiput which is most tender and allow your hand to gently cradle the entire occiput. Place your other hand over the sacrum with your thumb just below the junction of the sacrum and the 5th lumbar vertebra. Hold gently, feeling the energy moving along the spine, or stimulate sensitive points on the sacrum and occiput with alternating pressure. [BW: V.Hb]

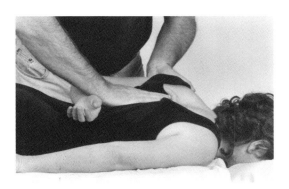

Scapula Release: (Bk II Ch 36) Grasp the shoulder with one hand, lifting it up and away from the table, while inserting the fingers of your other hand anywhere under the medial border of scapula. Move the shoulder in different directions, or in circles, as you slide deeper beneath the scapula with your other hand. The goal is to loosen and bring more flexibility to the shoulder area.
[BW: II.A5; B10]

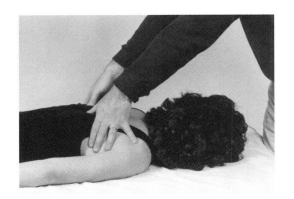

Release Shoulder Muscles and Rib Heads
(Bk II Ch 41, Fig. 2; Ch 57, Fig. 4)
Place your thumbs on the posterior rib heads and press downward toward the feet and into the table. You may use a slight thrust and/or hold a steady pressure. The same technique may be used over the scapula to release muscle spasms.
[BW: V.E1a]

Note: (Read Bk I Ch 8, pp. 81-89) Coccygeal and perineal techniques are very effective approaches to balancing energy. These approaches work best when both practitioner and client feel safe and all boundaries are clearly defined. If you know or suspect that your client may have ever been sexually abused or violated in any way, you should spend a lot of time developing trust before using these techniques. This may take several sessions or several years. You may also want to have another person whom your client trusts present as you work to make sure there are no boundary violations. Remember that, regardless of how much a move may seem to be indicated, its degree of effectiveness depends on the depth of safety, trust, and security between practitioner and client.

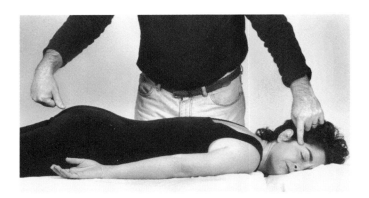

Coccyx/Sphenoid Balance: (Bk V Ch 16, 17, 18) Place the thumb, index, or middle finger of one hand along the edge of the coccyx. Place the thumb, index, or middle finger of your other hand on the greater wing of the sphenoid at the temple on the opposite side of the body. At the coccyx, hold satvically or press upward (superiorly) and toward the midline and gently rock back and forth. The contact at the sphenoid should remain light with the suggestion of anterior movement. Work both sides. [BW: III.B5]

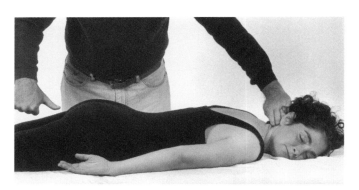

Balance Perineum and Neck: (Bk I Ch 8, pp. 81-89; Bk II Ch 30, 31; EES Ch 7, 8) Your client may lie on the table as shown or on their side with their knees drawn up. Find a point along the neck that is tense, sensitive or energetically charged. You may hold this point satvically, rajasically or tamasically. With the thumb, index or middle finger of your other hand, press into the tissues of the perineal floor (see diagram below). Beginning just below the tip of the coccyx (point 4 in diagram) and moving toward the pubic bone (point 1 in diagram), press into points along the edge of the perineal floor where it meets the bone. For each point, press lightly at first and gradually deepen your pressure. Ask your client for feedback. If you find a point that is particularly tender, tight, flaccid, or energetically charged, hold it for a few minutes, directing your pressure upward and toward the midline and gently rock the lower part of the body. Allow the energy to "ping pong" between the neck and perineum. [BW: III.A2a1,2]

PUBIC BONE

ISCHIOCARVERNOSUS MUSCLE

GENERATIVE ORGANS

BULBOSPONGIOSUS MUSCLE

DEEP PERINEAL MUSCLE WITH UNDERLYING FASCIA

SUPERFICIAL TRANSVERSE PERINEAL MUSCLE

EXTERNAL OBTURATOR MUSCLE

LEVATOR ANI MUSCLE

SACRO-TUBEROUS LIGAMENT

GLUTEUS MAXIMUS MUSCLE

COCCYX

ANUS

EXTERNAL ANAL SPHINCTER MUSCLE

Balance Perineum and Shoulders, Hips, Knees, Elbows, and Ankles (Bk I Ch 30, 31; Bk V Ch 14) Following the guidelines described in the previous section, energetically connect perineal points with points above and below the major joints of the body as shown in the photo and reflex chart below. The perineal contacts may be gentle to deep and rocking. The joint contacts are satvic, using your fingers or thumb on specific points or your whole hand over the general area. You do not have to use points at every joint as part of the protocol. Choose only those areas you are energetically drawn to. [BW: III.A2a]

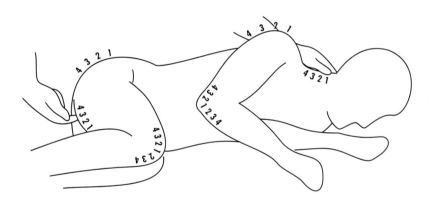

Balance Sensory Reflexes: (Bk II Ch 29) Contacts are made in a diagonal as shown or in a straight line from the shoulder to the base of the buttocks. The contacts utilize finger polarities, i.e.: the thumb is neutral, the second and fourth fingers are negative, and the third and fifth fingers are positive. For example, the negative second finger may contact the left shoulder and the positive third finger may contact the base of the buttocks. The spatial relationships between the points of contact should "match," i.e., if you are contacting the middle base of the buttocks, your other hand should contact the middle of the trapezius muscle on either shoulder. Hold satvically, allowing the energy to "ping pong" between your hands. [BW: II.B1]

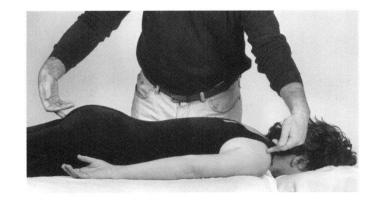

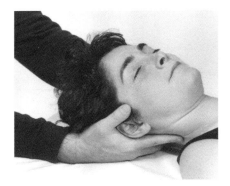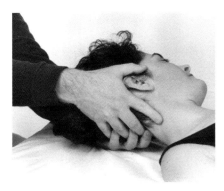

Cradle: Keep your hands soft and relaxed. Your index fingers go down the sides of the neck along the pathway of the Xth cranial nerve (which exits the skull just below the ear and runs down along the side of the neck). Your middle fingers cross at the occipital base and your thumbs rest by the ears. The head should be entirely cradled in your hands and not touching the table.

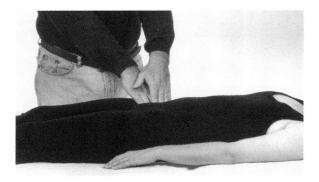

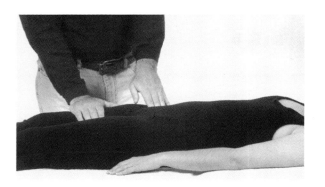

Psoas Release: (Bk II Ch 25) Place the fingertips of both hands just inside (medial to) the edge of the inguinal ligament which runs between the pubic symphasis and the anterior superior iliac spine. Slowly press into the tissues, directing your pressure toward the table (dorsally) and diagonally upward toward the opposite shoulder. Slowly work your way into deeper layers of the tissues until you find a place of tenderness or resistance. Hold this level of pressure and ask your client to take a deep breath. As they exhale, allow your hands to move deeper into the tissues. Repeat several times, continually asking your client for feedback. The pressure should not produce pain or the tissues will reflexively tighten. Do both sides. A variation of this work is shown in the second photograph: press into the tissues with the fingertips or the heel of the palm of one hand while the other hand gently rocks the upper thigh from side to side. [BW: IV.C2]

Five Star Balance:
(Bk I Ch 7; Bk II Ch 9, 10, 28)

To balance the five star, begin by looking at the five star chart on the following page and mentally relating the diagonal lines shown to points on your client's body. There are many variations of the five star work: The first picture shows a full diagonal contact from the left hip to the opposite shoulder. The second shows a contact along the same diagonal in which the right (lower) hand has moved up the diagonal line to a point just below the base of the sternum. The third and fourth pictures show smaller diagonal contacts across the sternum and abdomen.

Another variation (not shown) extends the five star diagonals down to the bottoms of the feet and out to the tips of the fingers, lifting and stretching the arms and legs and rotating the neck in a "figure 8" pattern. The psoas release, scapula release, and north pole stretch techniques shown elsewhere in this protocol also help to open the five star pattern.

Contacts may be made in any way that resonates with the energy. They may be held using your fingers, thumbs, or palms of your hands. Avoid crossing the midline of the body with your upper contact hand. Pressure may be tamasic, rajasic or satvic and you may even bring your hands off the physical body. As you hold the contacts, visualize energy moving along the diagonals. Tune into the energy and ask for ways to help your client's five star pattern become more open, vibrant, and flexible. You may also want to tell your client to feel free to sigh, yawn, groan or make any other sounds that feel appropriate to them. [BW: IV.A1; II.B2]

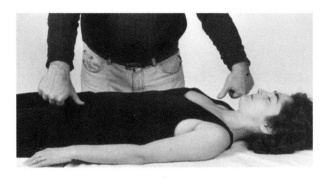

1

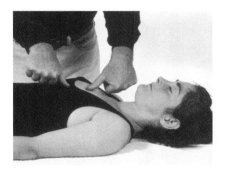

3

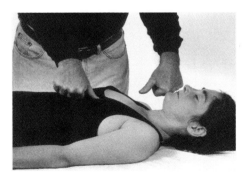

2

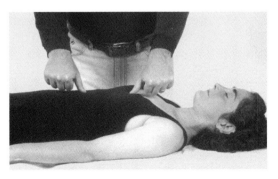

4

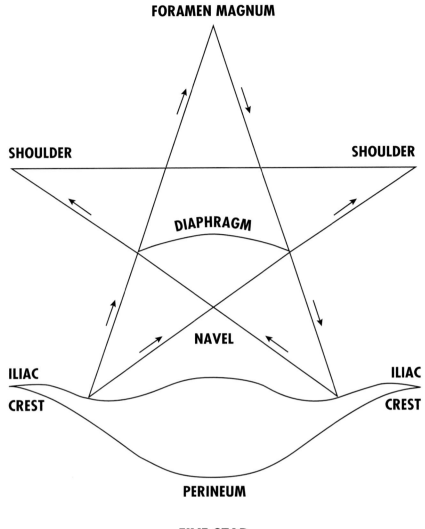

FIVE STAR

The five-pointed star, or "Five Star," pattern represented by the above chart is based on "Sacred Geometry"—archetypal patterns to which our bodies' subtle electromagnetic energy currents are aligned. The Five Star pattern is about expression and movement; it is meant to be flexible. Expression relates to both emotional expression through the throat center and to the expression of each of the organs through its function. Energy moves upward from the pelvic floor to the shoulders and through the throat to the top of the neck/foramen magnum. The balance and flexibility of the pattern is reflected in the balance and flexibility of the tissues along the diagonals. You can evaluate this visually, e.g., are the lines between hip and shoulder the same in both directions? And you can evaluate kinesthetically, e.g., are there areas of tension or pain along the diagonal? Or you can evaluate intuitively by looking with "soft eyes" and sensing the harmonic relationship of the lines; this is called visual harmonics.

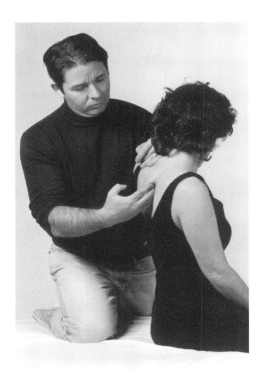 

Sitting Scapula Release: (Bk II Ch 46) Place the fingers or thumb of your right hand under the lower medial border scapula as shown. With your left hand, grasp and rotate the shoulder back toward your right hand. Repeat several times, moving further up the edge of the scapula each time. Ask your client to take deep breaths as you work. Do both shoulders. [BW: V.E2a]

Sitting Spinal Stretch For Gas Release: (Bk II Ch 45) Grasp the left shoulder as shown, allowing your client's body to rest comfortably on yours. Place the heel of your left palm along the left side of the spine anywhere between T5-T10. With your right hand, simultaneously lift and turn the torso to the right while pushing along the twisting line with your left hand. Do both sides. If appropriate, ask your client to make sounds. [BW: V.E1b V.E2a]

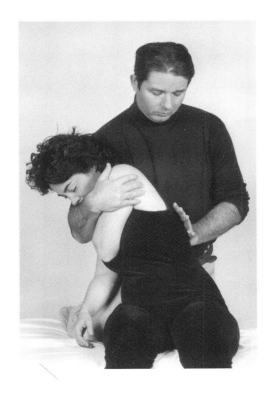

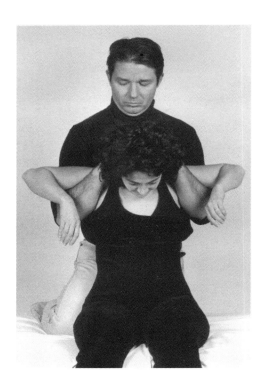

Sitting Crossover Lift: (Bk II Ch 50)
Place your arms underneath your client's shoulders and interlace your hands behind the occiput as shown. Ask your client to lean back onto your body and take a deep breath as you slowly lift them upward and back (posteriorly) to their maximum extension. At the top of the extension, use your chest to give a slight forward thrust on their upper thoracic spine or gently shake them from side to side. As they exhale, ask them to make sounds. [BW: V.E2b]

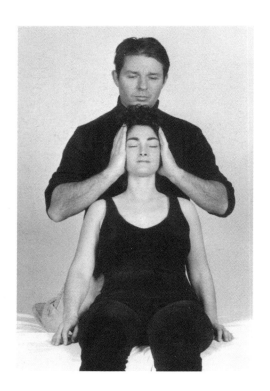

Sitting North Pole Stretch: (Bk II Ch 42; Bk III Ch 25; Bk IV, Ch 7; Bk V pp. 69-70)
Allow your client's body to rest comfortably against yours. Place your hands as shown, with your thumbs along the occipital base. Ask your client to take a deep breath as you lift their head upward to its maximum extension. You should take a deep breath with them. Holding their head in this exact spot, ask your client to exhale slowly, making a long, deep "aah" sound, as their body drops downward. Do this one to three times. [BW: II.A7; V.G1a]

AUTONOMIC NERVOUS SYSTEM

(Bk I pp. 70-89) (Polarity Process p. 134)
[EV: 1b,c; 3; 13]

The autonomic nervous system, along with the endocrine system with which it is intimately related, controls the body's internal organs and regulates many overall body functions such as blood flow, temperature, basal metabolism, muscle tone, and our ability to relax or stay alert and ready for action. The autonomic nervous system is divided into two parts called sympathetic and parasympathetic. Although the relationship between these two aspects of the autonomic system is complex, for our purposes we can look at their interaction in terms of reciprocal interplay. This means that they act somewhat like a teeter-totter: When the activity of the sympathetic nervous system increases, the activity of the parasympathetic nervous system decreases, and vice versa. Reciprocal interplay is organized by a center in the brain called the hypothalamus and a balanced discharge between sympathetic and parasympathetic is necessary for health. A loss of balance leads to physical, mental, and emotional imbalances; the nature of these imbalances depends upon which side dominates. "Our aim is to balance the two nervous systems in their bipolar effects with the circulation or the flow of "Prana" in the body. These vital factors are of first importance in restoring and maintaining good health, MENTALLY, PHYSICALLY, and EMOTIONALLY." (Bk I p. 88)

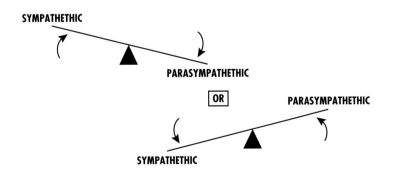

Sympathetic

Fire Principle

Yang

Activity

Physical Readiness and Action

Alertness

Expenditure of Energy

Adrenalin

Dehydration

Increased Oxygen Consumption

Assertive Emotions

    Irritability-Annoyance-Indignation-Anger-Rage

    Jumping Joy

Fast Pulse

Tension

Acid

Fight or Flight Response

Parasympathetic

Water Principle

Yin

Rest

Physical Relaxation

Sleep

Accumulation of Energy

Acetylcholine

Hydration

Decreased Oxygen Consumption

Vulnerable Emotions

    Fear-Hurt-Grief-Shame-Guilt

    Melting Joy, Love

Slow Pulse

Flaccidity

Alkaline

Repair and Regeneration of Tissues

Notes

DIGESTIVE BALANCE PROTOCOL

1. Cradle

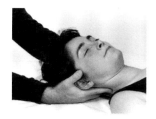

2. Taurus/Virgo Balance

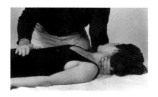

3. Abdominal Contacts

4. Gas Release

5. Work Colon Reflexes on Legs & Arms

6. Prostate/Uterine Reflexes

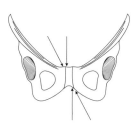

7. Pathway of Fire

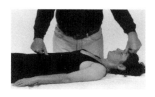

8. Fire Spiral

9. Umbilicus/Feet Circuit

10. Lymphatic Drainage

11. Cardiac Stability Hold

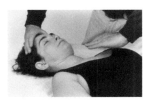

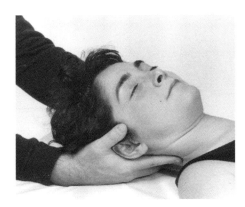 

Cradle: Keep your hands soft and relaxed. The touch is satvic. Your index fingers go down the sides of the neck, your middle fingers cross at the occipital base, and your thumbs rest by the ears. The head should be entirely cradled in your hands and not touching the table.

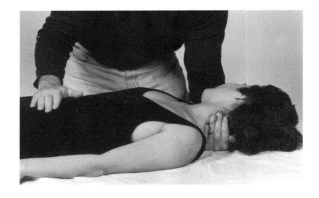

Taurus/Virgo Balance: Hold the back of the neck in the palm of your left hand as shown and place your right hand satvically on the lower abdomen about one inch above the public bone. As you hold this position, project a sense of "Earthy" security. Hold until you feel a unified pulse between your hands.

Abdominal Contacts: (Bk II Ch 20) Approach all abdominal contacts with gentleness and respect. This area is very vulnerable and exposed for everyone. Check for abdominal surgery or other forms of distress. If you know of or suspect sexual violation or any form of abuse, the abdominal area may be very charged. Take your time working into this area. Make sure you have established the necessary level of trust with your client. Work though cotton clothing; you do not need to make direct contact with the skin. In general, the contacts are free form and depend upon your perception of energy movement and tissue changes. You may spend anywhere from a minute to half an hour working the abdomen and its reflexes. [BW: IV.E5a]

Contact #1: Place your hands opposite one another on the abdomen and lower back as shown and tune into the energy of the abdominal region. Notice any areas of tension or flaccidity. Allow your hands to shift their position and/or pressure as the energy moves. Your top hand may even come off the body. Stay with this contact until you feel the tissues relax.

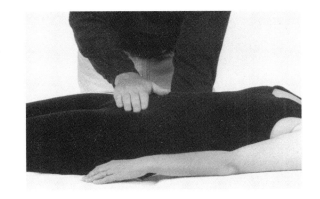

Contact #2: Place both hands anywhere on the abdomen. Gently press and rock, feeling for any areas of restriction, hardness or rigidity in the tissues. Slightly twist your hands in a clockwise direction in these areas. Stay with this contact until you feel the tissues relax.

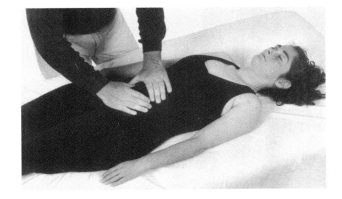

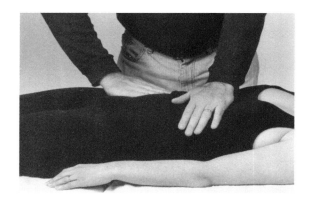

Contact #3: Begin by placing one hand over a specific abdominal organ (*e.g.,* liver, gallbladder, stomach, pancreas, colon, or small intestine) and tune into its energy and rhythm. Placing your other hand on an area that feels energetically connected to the first, satvically or rajasically direct energy to stimulate the organ. Then, rotate your hands in a direction which softens the tissues around the organ and allows it to unwind. Both hands may work together in gentle pushing or pulling motions. The direction may change as the tissues release. Always finish with a satvic hold.

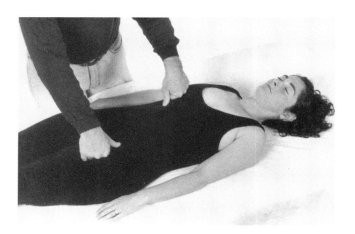

Contact #4: Make a diagonal contact between a point in an area of restriction to any other point on the abdomen which feels energetically connected to it. Direct energy along the diagonal. You may "ping pong" back and forth, rock or just hold satvically.

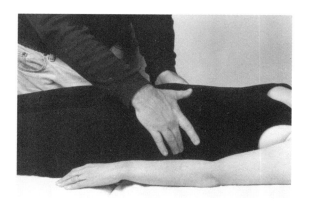

Gas Release Technique: (Bk III Ch 21) Place your hands around the sides of the abdomen as shown, anywhere in the space between the ribs and the tops of the iliums. Your fingers may reach to the transverse processes of the lower lumbar vertebra. Gently lift and rock. You may do this several times in different positions. [BW: II.A1]

Colon Reflexes: (Bk II Ch 6, 60, 61; EES Ch 18; Bk V Ch 13) Place your left hand over the lower abdomen one to two inches above the pubis. Place your right thumb on the Earth element line just above the ankle between the tibia and fibula. Work your way up to the knee (ascending colon reflex). On the left side place your right hand over the lower abdomen and work your way down the earth line from the knee to the ankle (descending colon reflex). [BW: IV.E5b]

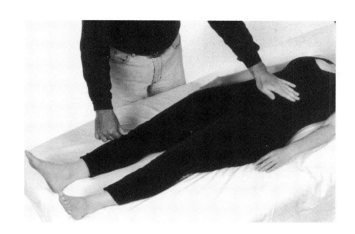

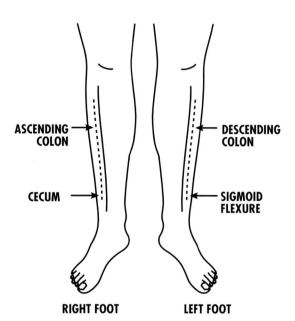

Prostate & Uterine Reflexes: (Bk II Ch 26, 61) Locate a sore point along the pubic bone and another sore point diagonally opposite it as shown in the diagram. Hold these points, adjusting your pressure and direction of energy, until you feel a unified pulse. You may also place one hand just above the pubic bone while contacting the uterine/prostate reflexes located below the inside ankle of either foot. The pressure and direction of energy you use may vary with your sense of the energy. [BW: IV.E6b]

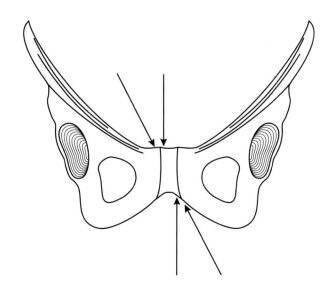

Pathway of Fire: (Bk III Ch 7, 8) The navel is the center of the Pathway of Fire. You can follow the pathway in any order from top to bottom or you can make contacts outward from the navel. Some important area are the eye orbits, chin, navel, thighs, and the last joint of the second toe. The contacts are made with your thumbs along the pathway lines except the chin and toes which are grasped between your thumb and index finger. [BW: IV.E1]

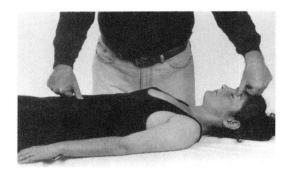
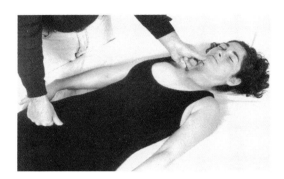
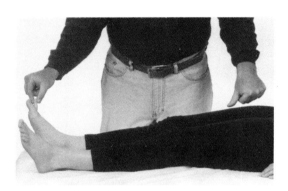

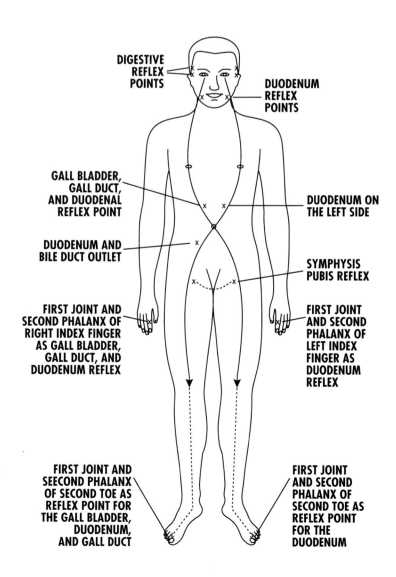

DIGESTIVE REFLEX POINTS

DUODENUM REFLEX POINTS

GALL BLADDER, GALL DUCT, AND DUODENAL REFLEX POINT

DUODENUM ON THE LEFT SIDE

DUODENUM AND BILE DUCT OUTLET

SYMPHYSIS PUBIS REFLEX

FIRST JOINT AND SECOND PHALANX OF RIGHT INDEX FINGER AS GALL BLADDER, GALL DUCT, AND DUODENUM REFLEX

FIRST JOINT AND SECOND PHALANX OF LEFT INDEX FINGER AS DUODENUM REFLEX

FIRST JOINT AND SEECOND PHALANX OF SECOND TOE AS REFLEX POINT FOR THE GALL BLADDER, DUODENUM, AND GALL DUCT

FIRST JOINT AND SECOND PHALANX OF SECOND TOE AS REFLEX POINT FOR THE DUODENUM

Fire Spiral: (EES Ch 2, 3, 18) Place one of your thumbs on the outer ring of the navel. Visualize Fire energy spiraling outward from the center of the navel (see diagram) and place your other thumb anywhere along the visualized Fire spiral with your thumbs pointing toward each other. Imagine warm Fire energy radiating outward from the navel on a spiral path betwen your thumbs. You can make as many contacts as you like along the spiral. The Fire spiral can also be worked from the back of the body. [BW: I.B7; III.B7]

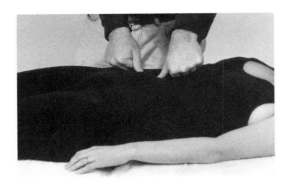 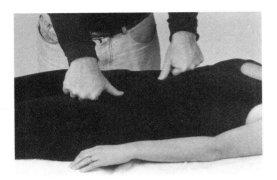

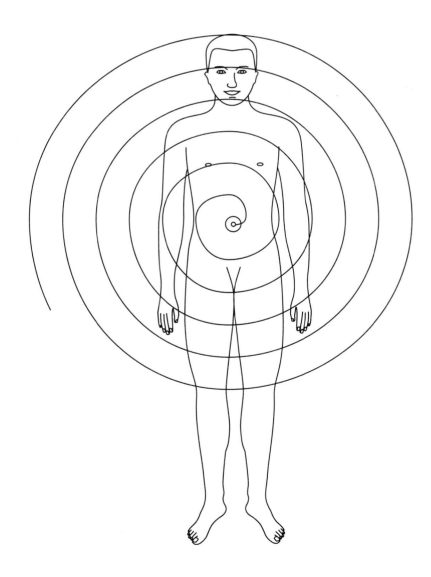

Umbilicus/Feet Circuit: (EES Ch 4) Place your left thumb in the navel ring pointing in any direction you want to direct Fire energy. Lift and open the legs as shown, bringing both feet together. Grasp the left and right foot with your right hand, placing your third and fourth finger between the feet and your second and third finger on the outside of the feet. "Ping pong" energy back and forth between the navel center and feet changing the direction of the navel contact as you feel the energy shift. [BW: I.B7; III.B7]

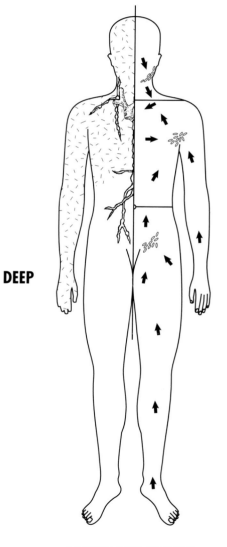

DEEP   SUPERFICIAL

LYMPHATIC SYSTEM

Lymphatic Drainage: (EES Ch 9) Lymphatic drainage can be performed anywhere on the body. It uses a flowing, receptive, Watery touch which allows your hands to become sensitive to the lymphatic fluid in the body's tissues. Begin by gently placing the pads of your fingers or the palmar surface of your hands on a relatively fleshy area of the body, such as the sides of the neck or the tops of the feet, and mentally ask the fluid to come to them. Your hands should feel as if they are resting gently on the surface of a lake, aware of and flowing with the movements and currents of the water. Maintain this awareness as you slowly move your hands or fingers along the surface of the skin, gliding or making clockwise circles. In denser muscular tissue, your touch can be somewhat firmer, like milking a cow or squeezing dough to make bread. Do not press too deep or hard or you may cut off the flow. The lymph fluid responds best to a light, aware touch and the proper intention. You may do a whole body lymph session or work specific areas, always moving the lymph in the direction of the heart. If you sense that the lymph is stagnant, cold or moving too slowly, you may want to hold that area while making contact with the Fire center of the navel, creating a Fire spiral in conjunction with the lymphatic work.

Caution: Be careful when doing lymphatic work on anyone who is detoxifying, has cancer and/or is taking radiation or chemotherapy treatments. Start with a little lymphatic work and find out how they respond to it. With certain forms of cancer it may be contraindicated altogether. [BW: III.B6]

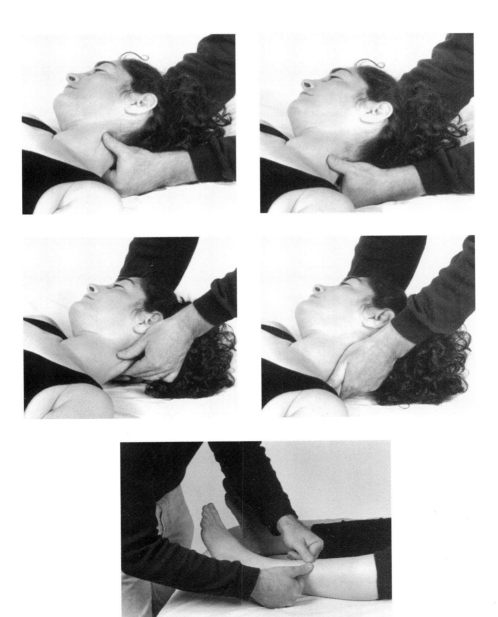

Cardiac Stability Hold: (Bk III, pp. 44; Bk II, Ch 43; Bk IV, Ch 9) Hold your left hand above the heart center and your right hand on the frontal bone along the cardiac stability reflex line as shown. The touch is satvic. Hold, allowing the energy to move back and forth, until you feel a unified pulse between your hands. You can also make contact with any part of the body while holding one hand over the heart center. [BW: I.A6]

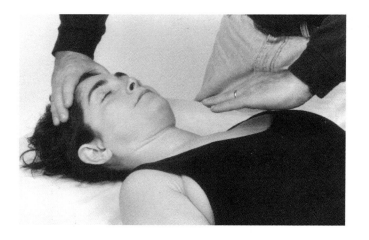

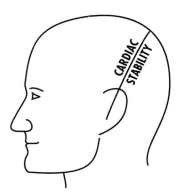

FOOD AWARENESS JOURNAL

Use this sheet to record your food awareness. Begin with a three-day period, and, if you would like, continue on a daily basis. Be as precise as possible. Be honest with yourself and try to include everything you can.

Day_____

Time	Foods Consumed	Eating Speed	Environment

FOOD AWARENESS JOURNAL EVALUATION
[EN: C]

Although the "Food Awareness Journal" on the previous page may be used to record eating patterns on an ongoing basis, the best way to use it initially is to ask your client to fill it out on the spot, recalling their eating and drinking for the past three to four days. There are several reasons for recalling past eating patterns rather than recording eating patterns day by day. The first is bias. A client may change their patterns to "look good" for the practitioner. The second reason is awareness. Recalling eating patterns requires the client to become aware of when and what they have eaten. Discovering blanks, vagueness, and confusion can be helpful. The third reason is self-correction. When your client becomes aware of their eating patterns they are often times able to make spontaneous corrections based on their personal knowledge of what works best for them.

Once they have filled out the journal, evaluate it based on the following criteria. You may find it helpful to use different colored pens for each one.

1. *Life Energy:* How close is a food to its natural living state? In general, the closer a food is to its natural source, the more life energy it contains. The further a food is removed from its source, the less life energy it contains. For example, sprouts and freshly picked fruit or vegetables would be placed at the living end of the continuum; on the other end would be such things as candies, synthetic ice cream, and white bread. Vegetables which are several days old, such as those bought at the supermarket, may be placed at +4 or +3. Fresh, untreated meats may be placed at 0, whereas processed meats sitting in the supermarket for days or weeks should be placed at -3 to -5. The numbers do not have to be exact. If you are unable to decide between two numbers, pick the lower number.

Living ——————————————————————————————————Processed

| +5 | +4 | +3 | +2 | +1 | 0 | −1 | −2 | −3 | −4 | −5 |

2. *Satvas, Rajas, and Tamas Balance:* Satvas, Rajas, and Tamas represent qualities of life energy. Rajasic foods have a fiery, stimulating quality; tamasic foods have a sedating, heavy, deadening or grounding quality; satvic foods are neutral and have a light quality. We can look at these qualities as inherent in the foods themselves and/or how they affect the person eating them. Thus, most fresh fruits and vegetables are satvic, creating a neutral state in the body and tending to neutralize both extremes—calming excess rajasic energy and cleansing out excess tamasic energy. Rajasic foods would include both stimulating foods and herbs and cooked grains (complex carbohydrates) which create and sustain a rajasic state in the body. Tamasic foods would be those that create and sustain a tamasic state in the body and include foods that are difficult to digest (high fat and protein content) such as meats, oils, and most processed foods. Things like coffee, chocolate, alcohol, and sugar all have an initially rajasic effect on the body, but ultimately cause a pendulum swing into Tamas if taken in excess.

Satvas——————————————Rajas ——————————————Tamas

3. *Elements:* Note whether each food eaten is Airy, Fiery, Watery, or Earthy in its energetic action, as determined by growing height and color, then determine the elemental balance of the diet as a whole. Color is judged by the outside "skin" of the food. For example, bananas are yellow; apples may be red, green, or yellow; blueberries are blue; raspberries are red; etc. The color and growing height may be combined to determine specific energetic tunings. For example, beets are red and grow below the ground; they are earth and earth. Carrots are orange and grow below the ground; they are water and earth. Processed foods, artificial colors, and meats are not included in this category.

Element	Growing Height	Color
Ether	(not measured by height)	Blue
Air	Six feet and above	Green
Fire	One foot to six feet	Yellow
Water	Ground Level to 12 inches above	Orange
Earth	Below Ground	Red

4. *Eating Rhythms:* When our inner time clock becomes confused, our whole body responds. Eating rhythms, especially intervals between meals, are very important to note. Observe the eating times and mark the areas of more than four hours between meals. We are rhythmic beings. When there are gaps of over four hours, irregular eating times from day to day, and a hectic life style (which prevents the body from going into the calm, parasympathetic state necessary for proper digestion), physical and emotional symptoms will result, regardless of the quality of the food eaten. For example, a client eats their first meal at 9 a.m. then eat again at 4 p.m. on the run and again at 11 p.m. because they need to settle down before they can sleep. Then, the next day, they skip their morning meal because they are in a hurry and eat at 2 p.m. and again at 10 p.m. I recommend that, before making any recommendations about changing the foods eaten, the practitioner should help the client create regular eating intervals and slower eating tempos. You can use the symptom history chart on the following page to show your client the effects of their eating rhythms.

Eating Tempo:

Very Fast————Fast————Moderate————Slow ————Very Slow

Time Intervals Between Meals:

Regular————————Irregular————————Erratic

5. *Food Combining:* The basic idea of food combining is to eat foods or combinations of food that are easiest to digest. A simple guideline is the systems law that the less diversity a system has, the more energy it will conduct. The best way to determine food combinations is through awareness. The Symptom History chart on the following page can be used to help a client tune into what happens after they have eaten. For example, a person may have eaten toast, eggs, orange juice, and coffee for breakfast and, two hours later noted bloating and excess gas. You may suggest that they eliminate the orange juice and find out what happens. Or you may suggest they have something simple for breakfast, such as oatmeal, and find out what happens. The assumption is that something in the combination of foods and/or a sensitivity to one or more of the foods is causing the symptom(s).

SPECIFIC SYMPTOM HISTORY
FOR USE WITH FOOD AWARENESS JOURNAL

When you notice a symptom, write down the exact symptom, the time you noticed the symptom, and how long it lasts. Compare this information with the foods, drinks, and supplements you put into your body as well as environmental conditions listed in your food awareness journal for the same day.

Day_____

Symptoms   Time of Day Noticed   Duration of Symptom(s)
(physical, mental, emotional)

BIBLIOGRAPHY

Arroyo, S. (1975). *Astrology, Psychology and the Four Elements*. Reno, NV: CRCS Publications.

Beaulieu, J. (1987). *Music and Sound in the Healing Arts*. Barrytown, NY: Station Hill Press.

Beaulieu, T. (1992) *The Color Love Journal*. New York: BioSonic Press.

Byers, D. (1983). *Better Health with Foot Reflexology*. Ingham Publications.

Chitty, J., & Muller, M.L. (1990). *Energy Exercises: Easy Exercises for Health and Vitality Based on Dr. Randolph Stone's Polarity Therapy*. Murrieta, CA: Lotus Press.

Cousins, G. (1986). *Spiritual Nutrition and the Rainbow Diet*. Boulder, CO: Cassandra Press.

Francis, J. (1985). *Polarity Self-Help Exercises*. Bath, England: Self-published.

Gehin, H. (1985). *Atlas of Manipulative Techniques for the Cranium and Face*. Seattle, WA: Eastland Press.

Goldman, J. (1992). *Healing Sounds: The Power of Harmonics*. Rockport, MA: Element Books.

Gordon, R. (1976). *Your Healing Hands*. Berkeley, CA: Wingbow Press.

Hoppenfeld, S. (1976). *Physical Examination of the Spine and Extremities*. Norwalk, CN: Appleton-Century-Crofts.

Jensen, B. (1981). *Tissue Cleaning through Bowel Management*. Escondido, CA: Bernard Jensen.

Juhan, D. (1987). *Job's Body*. Barrytown, NY: Station Hill Press.

Kapit, W., & Elson, L.M. (1977). *The Anatomy Coloring Book*. New York: Harper & Row.

Lipton, E., Bryan, A.F. (1986). *The Therapeutic Art of Polarity: An Instructional Manual for the Associate Polarity Practitioner*. Self-published.

Magoun, H.I. (1966). *Osteopathy in the Cranial Field*. Kirksville, MO: Journal Printing Co.

Murrieta Foundation. (1987). *Murrieta Hot Springs Vegetarian Cookbook*. Summertown, TN: The Book Publishing Co.

Netter, F. H. (1989). *Atlas of Human Anatomy*. Summit, NJ: CIBA-GEIGY.

Seidman, M. (1986). *A Guide to Polarity Therapy: The Gentle Art of Hands-On Healing*. North Hollywood, CA: Newcastle Publishing Co.

Siegel, A. (1987). *Polarity Therapy: The Power That Heals*. Dorset, England: Prism Press.

Sills, F. (1989). *The Polarity Process: Energy as a Healing Art*. Longmead, England: Element Books.

Stone R. (1987). *Polarity Therapy: The Complete Works. Vol. 1*. Reno, NV: CRCS Publications.

Stone R. (1987). *Polarity Therapy: The Complete Works. Vol. 2*. Reno, NV: CRCS Publications.

Stone R. (1987). *Health Building: The Conscious Art of Living Well*. Reno, NV: CRCS Publications.

Sutherland, W.G. (1967). *Contributions to Thought*. Fort Worth, TX: Rudra Press.

Sutherland, W.G., (Edited by Anne L. Wales, D.O.), (1990), *Teachings in the Science of Osteopathy*, Fort Worth, TX, Rudra Press.

Upledger, J., & Vredevoogd, J. (1983). *Craniosacral Therapy: Vol. 1*. Seattle, WA: Eastland Press.

Young, P. (1990). *The Art of Polarity Therapy: A Practitioner's Perspective*. Dorset, England: Prism Press.

POLARITY SUPPORT PRODUCTS

In order to help you further your Polarity Therapy studies, we have a complete selection of support products. These include:

- APTA Approved Trainings using video and mentors. Courses include Associate Polarity Practitioner, Registered Polarity Practitioner, Cranial-Spinal Balancing, Energy Nutrition and Energy-Based Counseling.

- The Polarity Wellness® Network Manual, a companion to the Polarity Therapy Workbook, containing APTA-registered Polarity Wellness® courses from Associate to Registered Polarity Practitioner levels. Each course includes purpose, goals, objectives, APTA standards references, assigned reading, and evaluations, which include protocols, written and oral exams, and client feedback forms.

- The Polarity Wellness® Wall Chart, a five-colour 18" x 27" chart with information from five of Dr. Stone's most commonly used charts, including a detailed five-element legend.

- BioSonic Repatterning™ products for sound healing, based on Polarity principles, which include Body Tuners™ and Solar Harmonic Spectrum™ tuning forks, and the CD's Calendula, "A Suite For Pythagorean Tuning Forks", Spirit Whistles, and Rainforest Mantras.

- A complete video certification course in BioSonic Repatterning™ which includes Cymatics, Sonic Anatomy, Five Element Evaluation, Tuning Forks, Voice Energetics, Toning, and Mantras.

Visit us on our web site:
   www.BioSonic Enterprises.com

or write us at

   BioSonic Enterprises, Ltd.
   P.O. Box 487
   High Falls, NY 12440